Instructor's Manual

to accompany

Motion and Time Study

Eighth Edition

Benjamin W. Niebel
The Pennsylvania State University

1988
IRWIN
Homewood
Illinois 60430

Printed in the United States of America.

ISBN 0-256-06083-5

1 2 3 4 5 6 7 8 9 0 MG 5 4 3 2 1 0 9 8

Introduction

This Instructor's Manual provides solutions to the Text Questions and Problems that are included at the end of each chapter of the eighth edition of *Motion and Time Study* written by Professor Benjamin W. Niebel and published by Richard D. Irwin, Inc. of Homewood, Illinois.

It also provides guidance to the development of answers to the General Questions that have been listed at the end of each chapter.

The instructor using this *Motion and Time Study* text will find that many of the problems and questions have been developed in a manner that permits alteration or modification. The instructor is encouraged to make such changes so that the students will be required to think creatively in order to arrive at an answer or develop a solution. In this way standard answers that can be passed on to successive classes will not prevail.

Contents

Chapter 1. Methods, Time Study, and Wage Payment Today 1

Chapter 2. The Development of Motion and Time Study 7

Chapter 3. Graphic Tools of the Methods Analyst 11

Chapter 4. Operation Analysis 15

Chapter 5. Operation Analysis (continued) 19

Chapter 6. Worker and Machine Relationships 27

Chapter 7. Motion Study 33

Chapter 8. Micromotion Study 39

Chapter 9. Human Factors Considerations 43

Chapter 10. Presentation and Installation of the Proposed Method 49

Chapter 11. Making the Job Analysis and the Job Evaluation 51

Chapter 12. Time Study Requirements 57

Chapter 13. Time Study Equipment 61

Chapter 14. Elements of Time Study 65

Chapter 15. Performance Rating 71

Chapter 16. Allowances 77

Chapter 17. The Standard Time 83

Chapter 18. Standard Data 87

Chapter 19. Basic Motion Times 95

Chapter 20. Formula Construction 99

Chapter 21. Work Sampling Studies 109

Chapter 22. Establishing Standards on Indirect and Expense Work 115

Chapter 23. Work Measurement and Computers 119

Chapter 24. Follow-Up Method and Uses of Time Standards 123

Chapter 25. Wage Payment 127

Chapter 26. Training and Research for Methods, Time Study, and Wage Payment 135

1

Methods, time study, and wage payment today

TEXT QUESTIONS

1. *What is another name for time study?*

   ANSWER: Work measurement.

2. *What job opportunities exist in the field of production?*

   ANSWER: Work measurement, work methods, production engineering, manufacturing analysis and control, facilities planning, wage administration, safety, production and inventory control, quality control in both manufacturing and service industries.

3. *What is the scope of methods engineering?*

   ANSWER: The scope of methods engineering involves designing, creating, and selecting the best manufacturing methods, processes, tools, equipment, and skills to manufacture a product or perform a service and then interface the proposed method with the best skills available.

4. *What activities are considered the key links to the production group within a manufacturing enterprise?*

   ANSWER: The activities that link to the production group include the producing of a quality product on schedule at the lowest cost with a minimum of capital investment, and with a maximum of employee satisfaction. It involves interaction with the efforts of sales, buying, design engineering, quality control, maintenance, cost control, and industrial relations, as well as line supervision.

5. *What is meant by the terms operation analysis, work simplification, and methods engineering?*

   ANSWER: These are synonymous terms indicating a technique for increasing the production per unit of time, thus reducing the unit cost of output.

6. *What nine step procedure is recommended for applying methods engineering?*

   ANSWER: Get the facts, present the facts, make an analysis, develop the ideal method, present the method, install the method, develop a job analysis, establish time standards, follow up the method.

7. *What steps has the Westinghouse Electric Corporation advocated to assure real savings during a methods improvement program?*

ANSWER: In connection with methods improvement, Westinghouse advocates: make a preliminary survey, determine the extent of analysis justified, develop process charts, investigate the approaches to operation analysis, make a motion study when justified, compare the old and the new method, present the new method, choose the installation of the new method, correct time values, follow up the new method.

8. *What is the function of the time study department?*

ANSWER: To determine equitable standard times for direct and indirect labor operations.

9. *Is it possible for one enterprise to have more than one type of wage payment plan? Explain.*

ANSWER: Yes. For example, a group incentive plan for the indirect operations in a shipping and receiving department and a one-for-one incentive plan for hourly production workers.

10. *What is the principal objective of methods engineering?*

ANSWER: To improve productivity while decreasing the unit cost of output.

11. *What four broad opportunities are there for savings through methods and time study?*

ANSWER: Increasing the output by reducing defects in design or specification of product, by improving the methods of manufacture, by reducing the shortcomings of management, by reducing the shortcomings of the worker.

12. *Explain in detail what a "work center" encompasses.*

ANSWER: A work center embraces all aspects of the immediate environment of a worker including: facilities he operates, layout of his work station, location of supply materials, and location of completed parts and means to get them to this location.

13. *What is the function of job evaluation?*

ANSWER: To determine the relative worth of the different work assignments within an organization.

14. *How is job evaluation dependent upon job analysis?*

ANSWER: Job analysis makes the job description from which the evaluation is made.

15. *What three considerations are included in a successful job evaluation plan?*

ANSWER: What the employee brings to the job in the form of education, experience, and special skills; what the job takes from the employee from the standpoint of physical and mental effort; responsibility that the job demands.

GENERAL QUESTIONS

1. *How do well-organized methods, time study, and wage payment procedures benefit the company?*

ANSWER: Increase the profits and provide for more hours of work for more people for more weeks of the year.

2. *Show the relationships between time study and methods engineering. Explain each fully.*

   ANSWER: Time study should not be undertaken until a good method has been developed and standardized. The methods analyst develops the good method. Thus these activities are closely related.

3. *Discuss the reasoning behind the statement, "A good time study man is a good methods engineer."*

   ANSWER: Both of these positions require similar capabilities from the standpoint of analysis, communication skills, and human relations.

4. *Comment on the general responsibility of the wage payment group.*

   ANSWER: The work in this area too requires a thorough knowledge and capability in human relations since it deals with the determination of the work content and the hourly money rates that are to be paid throughout the enterprise.

5. *Why does the purchasing department need data and information from the methods, time study, and wage payment department? Give several examples.*

   ANSWER: The purchasing department can obtain quality information on both materials and equipment from the methods and standards activities.

6. *Why is job evaluation a part of the wage payment function?*

   ANSWER: Because job evaluation is the way equitable base money rates are determined.

7. *What is meant by fundamental motion data?*

   ANSWER: Refer to chapter 19.

8. *Based on your reading of chapter 1, what percentage savings do you estimate is possible in a hospital which has never practiced methods engineering and time study? Do you feel this is a realistic estimate?*

   ANSWER: This question can provide some interesting discussion. 25 percent savings is realistic.

9. *Explain why, on the average, in the typical metal manufacturing plant only 15 percent of total cost is direct labor cost.*

   ANSWER: Because of increased mechanization and automation the majority of costs are material and indirect costs.

10. *Contact the following service industries in your community and find out what use is being made of professional competence in methods, standards, and wage payment: (a) a hospital (b) a high school (c) a post office (d) a police department (e) a bus service.*

    ANSWER: This question will stimulate much interest in the subject matter after the students report. Positive responses will usually result from post offices, hospitals, and transportation centers such as a bus service.

11. *What countries in addition to the ten shown do you feel would be in the top twenty in the world as far as R&D contribution per worker goes? Why?*

    ANSWER: The student should indicate that Canada, Yugoslavia, Russia, Brazil, South Korea, Taiwan, Hong Kong, Singapore, and perhaps China would be included in the top twenty because of these countries' recent commitment to industrial development.

PROBLEMS

1. *In the XYZ hospital, management has been charging $300.00 per day for a semi-private room. An analysis of present costs reveals the following:*

Direct Labor	$12.00 per hr.
Materials	$5.25 per patient per day
Indirect costs	$6.00 per 100 sq. ft. per day
Hospital room occupancy	80%

The typical patient utilizes 8.2 hrs. of direct labor help per 24 hrs. The average semi-private room is 14x20 ft. Was the $300.00 per day charge per person adequate? What dollar charge would you recommend? Explain how you would initiate a cost reduction program.

ANSWER: Present actual average daily cost per person in a semi-private room is:

$$\text{Direct labor} = (\$12.00)(8.2) = \quad \$98.40$$
$$\text{Materials} = \quad 5.25$$
$$\text{Indirect costs} = \frac{(14)(20)(6.00)}{(2)(100)} = \quad \frac{8.40}{\$112.05}$$

Since there is 80% occupancy and much of the cost prevails regardless of the occupancy, we should adjust the above estimate by 25% or $112.05/0.80 = $140.06.

This cost does not include the cost of medicines provided and the cost of food (meals). It appears the $300.00 cost per day is high. A charge of $200.00 per day per person would appear to be adequate. The nine step procedure outlined in this chapter would be the way to initiate a cost reduction program.

2. *In the Dorben Department Store, the local union and management entered into an agreement on the installation of work measurement standards and base rates determined by job evaluation. After the job evaluation was made the following job classes and money rates were established, based upon the job points noted:*

Job class	Job points	Money base rate/hour
A	100	$ 5.25
B	250	6.00
C	400	7.10
D	550	8.40
E	700	10.00
F	850	11.40

Because of the wide point range associated with each job class, the union representatives asked for the establishment of five additional job classes based on these job points: 175, 325, 475, 625, 775. What money rates per hour should be assigned to the five new job classes?

ANSWER: Since the data results in a parabolic relationship the problem can be solved algebraically or graphically. A graphic solution follows:

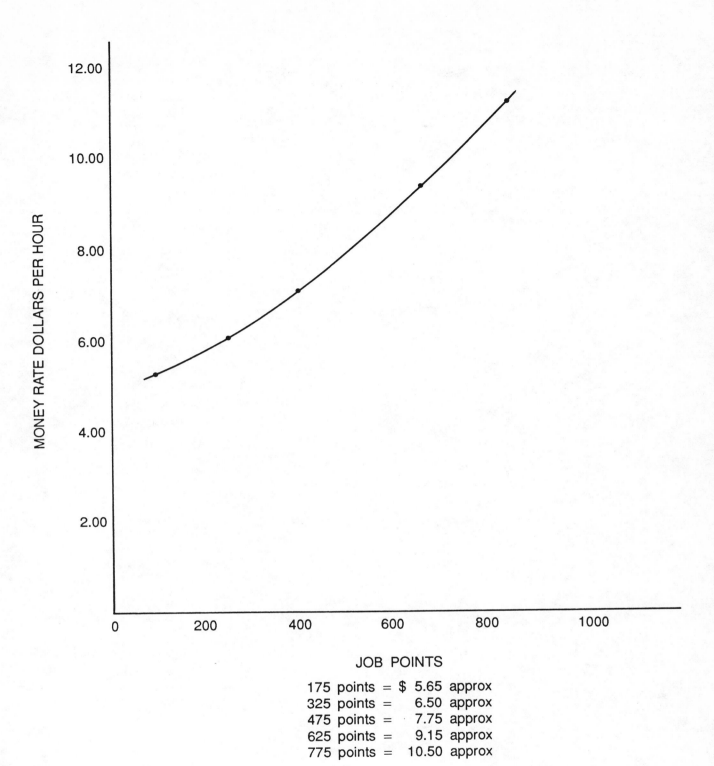

175 points = $ 5.65 approx
325 points =   6.50 approx
475 points =   7.75 approx
625 points =   9.15 approx
775 points = 10.50 approx

5

2

The development of
motion and time study

TEXT QUESTIONS

1. *Where were time studies originally made and who conducted them?*

   ANSWER: In France in the manufacture of pins by Perronet.

2. *Explain Frederick W. Taylor's principle of functional foremanship.*

   ANSWER: This was divided foremanship where there was a specialist for each activity. There is a specialist for feeds and speeds, a different specialist for tool geometry, etc.

3. *What effect has Congress had on time study?*

   ANSWER: In 1913 Congress added a rider to the government appropriation bill, stipulating that no part of the appropriation should be made available for the pay of any person engaged in time study work. In 1947 Congress passed a bill allowing the use of time study in the War Department.

4. *What is meant by motion study, and who is generally conceded to be the founder of the motion study technique?*

   ANSWER: This means the study of the body motions used in performing an operation, with the thought of improving the operation by eliminating unnecessary motions and simplifying necessary motions, and then establishing the most favorable motion sequence.

   Frank Gilbreth is considered the founder of the motion study technique.

5. *What is Carl G. Barth primarily noted for in the production end of industry?*

   ANSWER: For the development of a special slide rule for determining the most efficient combination of speeds and feeds for cutting metals of various hardnesses, considering depth of cut, size of tool, and life of tool. He is also noted for his work in determining fatigue allowances.

6. *Which organizations are concerned with advancing the ideas of Taylor and the Gilbreths?*

   ANSWER: Today the following organizations are active in advancing the ideas of Taylor and the Gilbreths: The American Management Association, The Society for the Advancement of Management, and The Institute of Industrial Engineers.

7. *Was the skepticism of management and labor toward rates established by "efficiency experts" understandable? Why or Why not?*

ANSWER: Yes, many unqualified analysts endeavored to establish standards. The results, in some instances, were quite unsatisfactory giving the profession a poor image.

8. *What psychological reaction is characteristic of workers when methods changes are suggested?*

ANSWER: Resistance to change.

9. *Explain the importance of the humanistic approach in methods and time study work.*

ANSWER: The humanistic approach must be followed in order to help assure the success of methods and standards work. Regardless of the analyst's technical knowledge and ability, he will not be completely successful in motion and time study work unless he is competent in dealing with the human element.

10. *What contributions in the area of motion study were made by the Gilbreths?*

ANSWER: They are generally considered to be founders of the modern motion study technique. They developed the motion picture technique for studying motions. They also developed the cycle graphic and chronocyclegraphic analysis techniques for studying the motion paths made by an operator.

11. *What was Emerson's philosophy of efficiency?*

ANSWER: His ideal was efficiency everywhere and in everything.

12. *What was Gantt's contribution to motion and time study?*

ANSWER: The development of graphic scheduling, showing performance against time and the invention of the task and bonus wage system.

13. *Who was Louis Brandeis, and what part did he play in the introduction of scientific management?*

ANSWER: Louis Brandeis represented the eastern business associations. He claimed that the railroad companies could save $1 million a day by introducing the new "science of management" into the railroad industry. Thus he was responsible for identifying Taylor's concepts as "scientific management."

14. *How did the Military Establishment Appropriation Act, 1947, submerge the development of work measurement methodology?*

ANSWER: By prohibiting the use of time studies in connection with government contracts.

15. *Who was the first director of the Work Measurement and Methods Engineering Division of the Institute of Industrial Engineers?*

ANSWER: Phil Carroll.

16. *What is the impact of MIL-STD 1567 on work measurement?*

ANSWER: Any firm awarded a contract exceeding $1 million must have a work measurement plan and procedures to establish and maintain engineered standards of known accuracy and traceability, a plan for methods improvement, and a plan for use of standards as an input to budgeting, estimating, planning, and performance evaluation.

17. *Who was Adam Smith?*

ANSWER: Adam Smith (1723-1790) was a Scottish economist. In 1776 he published "The Wealth of Nations." The concepts he expressed concerning the proper division of labor had an influence on the creation of the factory system and the impending Industrial Revolution.

18. *Why did the AIIE change its name to IIE?*

ANSWER: To give visibility to its international character and the importance of industrial engineering to all the industries and businesses throughout the world.

GENERAL QUESTIONS

1. *How is time and motion study used in industry today?*

ANSWER: Have your students make some inquiries to establish this answer. They should arrive at the fact that time and motion studies are primarily used by industry and business in connection with cost reduction and cost control.

2. *Why are labor unions training their representatives in time and motion study techniques?*

ANSWER: It would be good to have your students contact representatives of the labor movement in order to get a complete answer to this question. The principal reasons that labor unions support the training of their representatives in motion and time study is so that they will be more effective in connection with their representation of the employees. Most labor grievances are related to some aspect of job analysis, job evaluation, motion study, time study, or incentives. Unless labor representatives are well informed as to how these techniques are developed and applied they cannot be effective in representing their constituents when problems in these areas arise.

3. *Explain the function of the AMA as compared to that of the IIE.*

ANSWER: It would be a good idea to have a group of students interview both AMA and IIE members to understand the differences in the two organizations. Generally speaking the objectives of AMA are broader than those of IIE. Consequently from a membership standpoint AMA is almost three times larger than IIE. IIE is a professional society for Industrial Engineers while AMA covers the entire management field.

4. *Why was the government restriction on the use of stopwatches carried through the World War II years?*

ANSWER: This question can stimulate some interesting discussion. The students might find it interesting to interview some engineers who worked during the World War II years, although for the most part these people will now be retired. Perhaps the principal reason the government restriction on stopwatches prevailed throughout the World War II years was that the government did not want to bring up any issue that might antagonize labor. The desire was to increase productivity regardless of cost. The stopwatch was a very sensitive topic at the beginning of World War II.

5. *Interview a group of five industrial workers and obtain their opinions on the necessity of motion and time study.*

ANSWER: If the students are able to follow through on these interviews, the results will create some lively discussion.

6. *How would you rank in order of importance the following management techniques: material handling, work measurement, ergonomics, systems analysis, incentive applications, and method study? Justify your ranking.*

ANSWER: Methods study would be the most important and in reality it embraces material handling, ergonomics, and system analysis. The next in importance is work measurement because it is needed in order to reap the full savings brought about by methods study.

PROBLEM

The industrial engineer of a local township is considering the location of a hospital on a plot 3.2 miles from borough A and 5.8 miles from borough B. If borough A is 4.7 miles from borough B, find the angle at which straight roads joining the two boroughs with the hospital will intersect.

The population of borough A is three times that of borough B, and a second alternative is to place the new hospital 2.3 miles from borough A and 7.4 miles from borough B. If the cost of a hospital visit is computed at 0.20 per vehicle-mile and hospital visitors are known to be 25 percent of the population per year, which location would be the most favorable from the standpoint of visitation cost?

ANSWER: Use law of cosines (Appendix 2) to compute angle:

$$\cos A = \frac{b^2 + c^2 - a^2}{2bc}$$

$$= \frac{(3.2)^2 + (5.8)^2 - (4.7)^2}{(2)(3.2)(5.8)}$$

$$= 0.587$$

$$\therefore A = 54° \text{ approx.}$$

Let x = population of borough B

$3x$ = population of borough A

$$\text{Cost to B} = \frac{x}{4} \times 0.20 \times 5.8 = 0.29x$$

$$\text{Cost to A} = \frac{3x}{4} \times 0.20 \times 3.2 = \underline{0.48x}$$

$$\text{Total cost} = \$0.77x$$

$$\text{Cost (alternative) to B} = \frac{x}{4} \times 0.20 \times 7.4 = .37\ x$$

$$\text{Cost (alternative) to A} = \frac{3x}{4} \times 0.20 \times 3.2 = \underline{.345x}$$

$$\text{Total (alternative) Cost} = 0.715x$$

Therefore alternative location is better from the standpoint of visitation cost.

3

Graphic tools of the methods analyst

TEXT QUESTIONS

1. *Who uses process charts?*

   ANSWER: Methods engineers and other analysts that need to present the facts (data) in an orderly manner thus facilitating problem solution.

2. *What does the operation process chart show?*

   ANSWER: All materials, operations, inspections and operation and inspection times.

3. *What symbols are used in constructing the operation process chart?*

   ANSWER: A small circle (3/8" in diameter) denotes an operation and a small square (3/8" on a side) an inspection.

4. *How are materials introduced into the general floor flow when constructing the operation process chart?*

   ANSWER: Through horizontal lines feeding into the vertical flow lines.

5. *How does the flow process chart differ from the operation process chart?*

   ANSWER: The flow chart contains more detail than the operation process chart. In addition to operations and inspections, it includes transportations, storages, delays, and the times and distances involved. It is used to analyze both direct and indirect costs.

6. *What are the two types of flow charts?*

   ANSWER: Product flow charts and operative flow charts.

7. *What is the principal purpose of the flow process chart?*

   ANSWER: To effect maximum total savings (both direct and indirect costs) of one component of a product or system at a time.

8. *What symbols are used in constructing the flow process chart?*

   ANSWER: A small circle for an operation; a square for an inspection; a triangle standing on its vertex for a storage; a large D for a delay; and an arrow for a move or transportation.

9. *When would you advocate using the flow diagram?*

    ANSWER: In the solution of plant layout problems.

10. *How can the flow of several different products be shown on the flow diagram?*

    ANSWER: By using a different color for each of the products in connection with the flow lines.

11. *Why are the operation and flow process charts merely a means to an end?*

    ANSWER: They don't solve problems, they merely require gathering the necessary facts (data) and presenting them in an orderly way that facilitates problem solution.

12. *In the construction of the flow process chart, what method can be used to estimate distances moved?*

    ANSWER: Counting the columns that the product moves past and then multiplying the distance between columns by the number of columns minus one.

13. *How can delay times be determined in the construction of the flow process chart? Storage times?*

    ANSWER: Mark several parts with chalk indicating the exact time they went into storage or were delayed. Then check periodically to note when the marked parts are brought back into production.

14. *Explain how the concept of PERT charting can save a company money.*

    ANSWER: Primarily to improve scheduling at the least cost.

15. *What two flow chart symbols are used exclusively in the study of paper work?*

    ANSWER: ⊙ = paper work operation to create a record or set of papers and ⊘ = paper work operation to add information to a record.

GENERAL QUESTIONS

1. *What are the limitations of the operation and flow process charts, and of the flow diagram?*

    ANSWER: It is important that these graphic tools only help present problems—they do not solve them. If a problem cannot be stated, it usually cannot or will not be solved. These process charts in effect clearly state the problem or problems at hand.

2. *What relation is there between the flow chart and material handling? Between the flow diagram and plant bottlenecks? Between the operation process chart and material specifications?*

    ANSWER: Since the flow chart shows all distances traveled and indicates the material handling equipment, there is a close association between the flow process chart and material handling problems.

    The flow diagram highlights congested areas, backtracking, insufficient storage areas (both temporary and long term). All of these factors contribute to bottlenecks. Therefore the flow diagram assists in the development of solutions to relieve bottlenecks.

    The operation process chart not only shows the materials that enter into the general flow of a product development, but it gives the specifications of these materials. With this information clearly presented, existing material specifications can be studied with thought toward improvement.

3. *What is the connection between effective plant layout and the operation process chart?*

    ANSWER: The operation process chart providing the sequence of all operations and inspections gives, in effect, the layout of a plant based on "product" grouping which is generally considered the most advantageous under production manufacture.

4. *Distinguish between process and product grouping.*

ANSWER: Under process grouping, like facilities are grouped together. It is usually best for job shop manufacture. Product grouping arranges facilities to minimize transportation distances between operations. It is usually best when production quantities are high.

5. *What is meant by group technology?*

ANSWER: This is mentioned on page 32 as being "the classification of different products into similar geometric configurations and sizes so as to take advantage of the economics in manufacture brought about by large quantities." The student is urged to read more on the subject by referring to page 83.

6. *Why is the flow process chart a valuable tool in training new employees?*

ANSWER: Because it provides such detailed information for all the steps required to produce a product and/or for performing a job or operation.

PROBLEM

Based upon the following emergency cost table, what would be the minimum time to complete the project described by Figure 3-7 and whose normal costs are shown in Table 3-2? What would be the added cost to complete the project within this time period?

Emergency Cost Table

Activity	Weeks	Dollars
A	2	$7,000
B	1	2,500
C	2	5,000
D	0.5	2,000
E	4	6,000
F	3	5,000
G	2	6,000
H	0	0
I	4	7,600
J	1	2,200
K	4	4,500
L	2	2,200
M	3	3,000
N	1	1,000
O	2	6,000
P	1	3,000

ANSWER: 27 week schedule — normal duration of project — cost = $22,500.

26 week schedule — the least expensive way to gain one week would be to reduce activity I by one week for an additional cost of $200 — total cost is $22,700.

25 week schedule — the least expensive way to gain two weeks would be to reduce activity I by two weeks at an additional cost of $400 — total cost is $22,900.

24 week schedule — the least expensive way to gain three weeks would be to reduce activity I by two weeks and activity J by one week at an additional cost of $1,000 — total cost = $23,500.

23 week schedule — the least expensive way to gain four weeks would be to reduce activity I by two weeks, activity J by one week and activity K by one week for an additional cost of $1,750 — total cost — $24,250.

22 week schedule — the least expensive way to gain five weeks would be to reduce activity I by two weeks, activity J by one week, activity K by one week and activity M or P by one week for an additional cost of $3,150 — total cost = $25,650.

21 week schedule — the least expensive way to gain six weeks would be to reduce activity I by two weeks, activity J by one week, activity K by one week, activity M by one week and activity P by one week for an additional cost of $4,550 — total cost = $27,050.

20 week schedule — the least expensive way to gain seven weeks would be to reduce activity I by two weeks, activity J by one week, activity K by one week, activity M by one week, activity P by one week and activity F by one week for an additional cost of $6,350 — total cost = $28,850 (note we now have an additional critical path — B-2, E-5, G-3 takes ten weeks as does C-3, F-3, and I-4).

19 week schedule — the least expensive way to gain eight weeks would be to reduce activity I by two weeks, activity J by one week, activity K by one week, activity M by one week, activity P by one week, activity F by one week and activity C by one week. (Note activity E can be shortened by one week at no extra cost. Thus no extra charge is incurred on the path B-2, E-4,G-3.) Additional cost for 19 week schedule — $8,750 — total cost $31,250.

The student should note that by allowing activity L to be done in two weeks rather than three weeks, a savings of $800 can be made. Thus, the total cost of project is $30,450.

Also note that activity N under emergency will cost $1,000 or $300 more than under normal even though the time of one week has not been changed. The extra $300 is charged to provide more assurance that the one week schedule will be maintained. Total cost of project with this reliability is $30,750.

4

Operation analysis

TEXT QUESTIONS

1. *Explain how design simplification can be applied to the manufacturing process.*

   ANSWER: Simplicity in the product design invariably results in better producibility. A complex design will usually require more sophisticated processing or at least more complex tooling than the simple design.

2. *How is operation analysis related to methods engineering?*

   ANSWER: Operation analysis is a technique for accomplishing the goal of methods engineering.

3. *Does increased competition submerge the necessity for operation analysis? Explain.*

   ANSWER: No. Increased competition will promote the need for operation analysis. Progress in productivity improvement, resulting from operation analysis, is the only key to continued profitable operation.

4. *Explain the relationship between market price and volume as related to production.*

   ANSWER: For the vast majority of products there is a relationship between market price and consumer demand. The lower the price the greater the demand.

5. *What is the major obstacle in the path of the methods analyst?*

   ANSWER: Resistance to change.

6. *How do unnecessary operations develop in an industry?*

   ANSWER: Improper planning when the job was first set up, improper performance of a previous operation, and the introduction of an operation to facilitate an operation that follows. Also unnecessary operations may result from an attempt to give a product more sales appeal.

7. *What four thoughts should the analyst keep in mind to improve design?*

   ANSWER: (a) Reduce the number of parts, thus simplifying the design.
           (b) Join parts better and make the machining and assembly easier.
           (c) Utilize a better material.
           (d) Rely for accuracy upon "key" operations rather than upon a series of closely held limits.

8. *Explain why it may be desirable to "tighten up" tolerances and specifications.*

   ANSWER: To facilitate assembly or other secondary operations.

9. *What is meant by lot-by-lot inspection?*

   ANSWER: A sampling procedure in which a sample is inspected in order to determine the quality of the production run or the lot.

10. *When is an elaborate quality control procedure not justified?*

    ANSWER: If the product does not require close tolerances, if its quality is easily checked, and if the generation of defective work is unlikely.

11. *What six points should be considered when endeavoring to reduce material cost?*

    ANSWER: Finding a less expensive material, finding materials that are easier to process, using materials more economically, using salvage materials, using supplies and tools more economically, and standardizing materials.

12. *Explain why corrugated metal sheet is more rigid than flat sheet of the same material?*

    ANSWER: Since more material is away from the neutral axis, the corrugated sheet is more rigid.

13. *How does a changing labor and equipment situation affect the cost of purchased components?*

    ANSWER: Significantly affects the cost of purchased parts. Labor intense products are dramatically affected by the hourly rates of labor. Similarly the output per unit of time of production equipment has a major impact on product cost.

14. *The finish tolerance on a shaft was changed from 0.004 in. to 0.008 in. How much cost improvement resulted from this change?*

    ANSWER: Refer to Figure 4-11. From this graph the approximate cost of production will be reduced from 1.4 to 1.1 or $\frac{.3}{1.4}$ = 21%.

15. *What is the therblig symbol and color designation for "rest to overcome fatigue"?*

    ANSWER: The symbol is R or φ_L , and the color designation is orange.

16. *What has been the impact of the computer in connection with paper work?*

    ANSWER: Today, with the advance of computer controlled systems, there should be a continued reduction in the generation of forms and paper work.

17. *What overall tolerance would be applied to three components comprising the overall dimension of a product if component one had a tolerance of 0.002"; component two 0.004"; and component three 0.005"?*

    ANSWER: The overall tolerance is equal to the square root of the sum of the squares of the individual tolerances comprising the overall tolerance.

$$\text{Overall tolerance} = \sqrt{(0.002)^2 + (0.004)^2 + (0.005)^2} = 0.0067"$$

16

18. *What six points should be kept in mind when designing forms?*

ANSWER: Maintain simplicity, provide ample space allowing for different input methods, provide information in a logical sequence, use color coding to facilitate routing and distribution, provide adequate margins to accommodate standard filing, confine forms to one page for computer terminals.

GENERAL QUESTIONS

1. *Formulate a checklist that would be helpful in improving operations.*

ANSWER: The questions shown on Figure 4-1 can be used as a start.

2. *Explain how the conservation of welding rod can result in 20 percent material savings.*

ANSWER: Much of the welding rod is held in a holder and is often discarded when there is still several inches of usable rod. Often this discarded portion is 20% of the usable rod. Ask students when they discard a pencil. Frequently they throw it away when there is as much as 20% of usable pencil left.

3. *Investigate the operations required to convert waste SO_2 to usable S.*

ANSWER: This procedure has been practiced by some industries. Have the students investigate what steps are involved and the possibility of the procedure being cost effective.

4. *Explain why this country has lost a large share of its steel business to Japan and Korea since the early 1970's. What needs to be done to regain the business lost?*

ANSWER: Japan and Korea introduced more modern technology resulting in the ability to produce quality steel more efficiently. Furthermore, their labor rates (both direct and indirect) are considerably less. In order to regain the business lost, US steel companies need to modernize. Automation techniques need to replace many hand methods. There must be more practice of methods engineering, equitable standards and competitive labor rates. There need to be more effective management motivation methods.

PROBLEMS

1. *A ceramic material is being considered as a possible mold material in conjunction with the die casting of 60-40 brass. A cylinder of the material 8 inches in diameter and 10 inches long was used to obtain a stress-strain relationship in compression. The material failed under a load of 265,000 pounds and a total strain of 0.012 inches. What was the material's fracture strength, percent contraction at fracture, and modulus of toughness?*

ANSWER: The solution to this problem is based on elementary strength of materials.

$$\text{Fracture strength} = \frac{265,000 \times 4}{\pi \times (8)2} = 5,270 \text{ lb/sq. in.}$$

$$\text{Percent contraction} = \frac{0.012 \times 100}{10} = 0.12\%$$

$$\text{Modulus of toughness} = \frac{2}{3} S_\mu \ E_\mu = \frac{2(5270)(0.0012)}{3} = 4.216 \text{ in lb/cu. in.}$$

17

2. *The Dorben Company is designing a cast-iron part whose strength T is a known function of the carbon content C.*

$$T = 2C^2 + \frac{3}{4} C - C^3 + k$$

In order to maximize strength, what carbon content should be specified?

ANSWER: $\dfrac{dT}{dC} = 4C + \dfrac{3}{4} - 3C^2$

$$3C^2 - 4C - \frac{3}{4} = 0$$

$$C = 1.5\% \text{ carbon content}$$

3. *In order to make a given part interchangeable, it was necessary to reduce the tolerance on the outside diameter from ± 0.010 to ± 0.005 at a resulting cost increase of 50 percent of the turning operation. The turning operation represented 20 percent of the total costs. By making the part interchangeable, the volume of this part could be increased by 30 percent. The increase in volume would permit production at 90 percent of the former cost. Should the methods engineer proceed with the tolerance change? Explain.*

ANSWER: Obviously the change should be made since total cost is reduced 10 percent. Total cost is always the bottom line.

5

Operation analysis (continued)

TEXT QUESTIONS

1. *In what four ways should an investigation to improve the process of manufacture be made?*

   ANSWER: When changing an operation, consider the possible effects on other operations, mechanize manual operations, utilize more efficient facilities on mechanical operations, operate mechanical facilities more efficiently.

2. *Explain how rearranging operations can result in savings.*

   ANSWER: This can result in the elimination of an operation. For example burs thrown up after drilling can often be removed through some such operation as turning or grinding if they follow the drilling operation.

3. *What process is usually considered the fastest for forming and sizing operations?*

   ANSWER: Press operation.

4. *How should the analyst investigate the set up and tools to develop better methods?*

   ANSWER: He should determine the quantity to be produced, the chances for repeat business, the amount of labor involved, delivery requirements, the amount of capital required.

5. *Give some applications of bar coding for the improvement of productivity.*

   ANSWER: Inventory can be counted and controlled, specific items can be routed to or through a process, work-in-process can be controlled.

6. *When would you recommend the use of energy efficient motors?*

   ANSWER: On continuous installations such as compressors, pumps, fans, blowers, etc.

7. *How much more efficient is a typical 50 HP energy efficient motor than a standard 50 HP motor?*

   ANSWER: From Figure 5–9, a little more than 3% (92.5 − 89.4).

8. *Why should the methods analyst accept as part of his or her responsibility the provision of good working conditions?*

ANSWER: Good working conditions will result in higher productivity. Employees will become greater over-all contributors when they recognize that management endeavors to provide first-class working conditions.

9. *Give the requisites of effective guarding.*

ANSWER: Effectively protect the employee, permit normal operation of the facility at a pace equal to or greater than that given without the guard, permit normal maintenance of the facility.

10. *What are the two general types of plant layout? Explain each in detail.*

ANSWER: Product or straight-line layouts and process or functional layouts. In the straight-line layout, the equipment and work stations are located so that the flow from one operation to the next is minimized for any product class. Process or functional layout is the grouping of similar facilities.

11. *To what scale are templates usually constructed?*

ANSWER: $1/4$ inch equals 1 foot except when project is large. Here $1/8$ inch equals 1 foot may be used.

12. *Explain the fundamental purpose of group technology.*

ANSWER: To provide enough volume of a product line to take advantage of the economics of product group layout and universal tooling.

13. *What is the best way to test a proposed layout?*

ANSWER: Trace the flow of the various products or product lines produced. This can be done using different colored threads which can be attached to the map tacks holding down the templates.

14. *What questions should the analyst ask himself when studying work performed at a work station?*

ANSWER: Are both hands working at the same time and in opposite symmetrical directions? Is each hand going through as few motions as possible? Is the workplace arranged so that long reaches are avoided? Are both hands being used effectively and not as a holding device?

15. *For what purpose is operation analysis used?*

ANSWER: Increased output per unit of time and/or reduced unit cost.

16. *Explain the advantage of using a checklist.*

ANSWER: The checklist helps assure the analyst considers all the improvement possibilities. It will also stimulate creative thinking for further improvement possibilities.

17. *Why do costs vary little with distance in connection with automated guided vehicles?*

ANSWER: They utilize little power and maintenance does not vary directly with usage.

18. *What are the primary approaches to operation analysis?*

ANSWER: The text identifies ten primary approaches to operation analysis. These are: purpose of operation, design of part, tolerances and specifications, material, process of manufacture, set-up and tools, working conditions, material handling, plant layout, principles of motion economy.

19. *On what does the extent of tooling depend?*

ANSWER: Upon the quantity to be produced, the probability or chance for repeat business, the labor content of the operation under study.

20. *Do working conditions appreciably affect output? Explain.*

ANSWER: Yes. Experience has proven conclusively that plants providing good working conditions will outproduce those maintaining poor conditions.

21. *How can planning and production control affect setup time?*

ANSWER: By planning similar jobs to follow one another much setup time can usually be saved since similar jobs will frequently have common tooling.

22. *How can you best handle a material?*

ANSWER: By minimizing the manual handling.

23. *Why should "terminal" time be minimized?*

ANSWER: In order to keep production facilities operating productively.

24. *Explain the effect of humidity on the operator.*

ANSWER: When humidity increases, evaporative cooling decreases rapidly, thus reducing the ability of the body to dissipate heat. These conditions cause high heart rates, high body temperatures, and pronounced fatigue.

25. *Why does the travel chart have more application in process grouping than in product grouping?*

ANSWER: Product grouping already provides for short distances between successive operations in the production of a product.

26. *Explain why a sound classification system is the first requisite of a successful group technology program.*

ANSWER: The classification system is the basis of determining the commonness in jobs. Without a sound classification system, there would be many omissions and errors in endeavoring to group similar work.

GENERAL QUESTIONS

1. *Where would you find application for a hydraulic table?*

ANSWER: Those students with summer work experience should be able to give several examples. Typical would be: in storerooms, stockrooms, tool cribs, punch press facilities (job shop) where dies are frequently changed.

2. *What is the difference between a skid and a pallet?*

ANSWER: Have the students see if they can identify the difference by studying Figure 5-12. Note that the pallet always has a bottom covering and to be moved must be lifted by a fork truck. A skid does not have a bottom, usually is of heavier construction, and can be moved with a load by either a fork truck or other means.

3. *Explain the significance of the colored code for stock templates.*

   ANSWER: Color coding of templates provide a further identifying mechanism.

4. *When would you recommend using three-dimensional models in layout work?*

   ANSWER: When the layout is extensive. Particularly when layout must be sold to a busy executive. When layout involves several facilities where height as well as floor area must be considered.

5. *What is the general flow of analysis procedure when it is applied to a product that has never been manufactured?*

   ANSWER: The student should recognize the procedure is about the same as when studying a product already in production although there will be less hard data available to study and analyze.

6. *In a process like operation analysis, is it necessary to determine the point of diminishing returns? Why or why not?*

   ANSWER: Diminishing returns certainly does apply in operations analysis work. We should not spend money on improvement when the time and money exceeds the rewards. We must always be cost effective.

7. *Select five work stations and measure the footcandle intensity at these stations. How do these values compare with recommended practice?*

   ANSWER: The instructor should be able to acquire a footcandle meter and make this assignment to several student groups.

8. *Develop a classification system suitable for group technology where we have five product lines utilizing components with 13 geometric configurations and involving three types of thermosetting plastics. Make any assumptions that you feel appropriate.*

   ANSWER: Suggest that this classification system be used primarily to identify how best a given design should be processed. The following processes would need to be considered: compression molding, transfer molding, injection molding, extrusion, casting, cold molding, thermoforming and blow molding. Of these thermoforming, blow molding, and extrusion are limited to thermoplastic resins.

9. *Derive the equations for the three straight line graphs in Figure 5-6 and calculate algebraically the three break-even points.*

   ANSWER: Using the equation of a straight line: Total Cost (TC) = Slope × Total Activity (TA) + Intercept.

   Selecting points from the chart:

   $$\text{TC (old method)} = \frac{1,700 - 0}{12,000 - 0} \times \text{TA} + 0$$

   $$\text{TC (old method)} = 0.142 \text{ TA}$$

   $$\text{TC (No. 1 alt)} = \frac{1,540 - 300}{12,000 - 0} \times \text{TA} + 300$$

   $$\text{TC (No. 1 alt)} = 0.103 \text{ TA} + 300$$

   $$\text{TC (No. 2 alt)} = \frac{1,430 - 600}{12,000 - 0} \times \text{TA} + 600$$

   $$\text{TC (No. 2 alt)} = 0.069 \text{ TA} + 600$$

Intersection of old method and No. 1 alternative method:

TC (old method) = 0.142 TA

$\underline{\text{TC (No.1 alt)} = 0.103.\ \text{TA} + 300}$

TA (intersection) = 300 ÷ 0.039 = 7,692 pieces

Intersection of old method and No. 2 alternative method:

TC (old method) = 0.142 TA

$\underline{\text{TC (No. 2 alt)} = 0.069\ \text{TA} + 600}$

TA (intersection) = 600 ÷ 0.073 = 8,219 pieces

Intersection of No. 1 and No. 2 alternative methods:

TC (No. 1 alt) = 0.103 TA + 300

$\underline{\text{TC (No. 2 alt)} = 0.069\ \text{TA} + 600}$

TA (intersection) = 300 ÷ 0.034 = 8,824 pieces

10. *Check with some local factory where metal removal operations are employed and determine the application of "whisker-reinforced ceramics."*

ANSWER: the student is likely to find these ceramic tools being used in the production machining of cast irons.

11. *Why is it that Japan has taken a leadership role in the use of robots?*

ANSWER: Primarily because of the extensive use of the robot for spot welding operations in the automobile assembly operations. The Japanese realized the economy and consistency of quality of robot controlled spot welding and adapted this procedure in the production of cars. The U.S. automotive industry has been slower to follow this pattern.

PROBLEMS

1. *In the Dorben Company, the methods analyst was assigned the task of altering the work methods in the press department in order to meet OSHA standards relative to permissible noise exposures. She found the average sound level to be 100 dBA. The standard deviation was 10 dBA.*

The 20 operators in this department were provided with earplugs, and the power output from the public-address system was reduced from 30 watts to 20 watts. The deadening of the sound level by use of the earplugs was estimated to be 20 percent.

What improvement resulted? Do you feel that this department is now in compliance with the law at the 99 percent confidence level? Explain.

Hint: Decibel loss = 10 log $\dfrac{\text{Power output original}}{\text{Power output planned}}$

ANSWER: Decibel loss = 10 log $\dfrac{30 \text{ watts}}{20 \text{ watts}}$

$$= 1.76$$

$$\overline{X}_{dBA} = 100$$

$$\pm\ 3\sigma_{dBA} = \pm\ 30 \text{ dBA}$$

∴ range of sound level = 70 to 130 dBA. With power output modification, range = 68.2 to 128.2 dBA; with ear plugs (upper limit) = 128.2 − .2 (128.2) = 102.6 dBA. ∴ Company is in compliance since Table 9-7 indicates 105 dBA is permissible up to 1 hour per day. This company will have a level of 102.6 only about 2 percent of the day.

2. *In the Dorben Company, the methods analyst designed a work station where the seeing task was difficult because of the components going into the assembly. She established the desired brightness as being 100 footlamberts on the average with a standard deviation of 10 footlamberts so as to accommodate 95 percent of the workers. The work station was painted a medium green having a reflectance of 50 percent. What would the required illumination in footlamberts be at this work station in order to provide adequate illumination for 95 percent of the workers? Estimate what the required illumination would be if the work station were repainted with a light cream paint.*

ANSWER: In order to work this problem the student should first review table 9-3.

From table 9-3 with a reflectance of 50% we note a footcandle rage of 85 to 240 to accommodate a brightness range of 42 to 100 footlamberts.

Since the range needed at the specified work station is 100 footlamberts $\pm$ (2)(10) or 80 to 120 we can estimate the footcandle lower range as being: 84:42::X:80
$$X = 160 \text{ footcandles}$$

and the upper range is: 240:100::X:120
$$X = 288 \text{ footcandles}$$

If the work station is painted a light cream, we note the percent of reflected light (from Table 9-1) is increased to 75%. By interpolation the footcandle range will be reduced to approximately 135 to 232 footcandles.

3. *The analyst in the Dorben Company is considering replacing five 50 HP with five 50 HP energy efficient motors. These motors will all be operated seven days per week and three shifts per week at 85% of full load. If the cost of electric power is $0.06 per KWH, how much can the company afford to pay for the five energy efficient motors?*

ANSWER: Power cost/yr. (standard motor) = $50 \times 0.746 \times 0.85 \times 365 \times 24 \times 0.06 \div 0.895 = \$18,619.16$

Power cost/yr. (energy efficient motor) = $50 \times 0.746 \times 0.85 \times 365 \times 24 \times 0.06 \div 0.925 = \$18,015.29$

Savings in power per year = $603.87

Assume the company requires a return of capital in three years. Then the company could afford to pay for the five motors:

$5 \times 3 \times \$603.87 = \$9,058.00$

4. *The methods analyst in the Dorben Company is considering the installation of a state-of-the-art solid state electronic energy conservation system that will tune and balance the whole fluorescent system, including lamps, ballast, and power supply in the plant. The system will regulate the voltage and the current on an ongoing basis to establish and hold the system at optimum performance and it will also protect the system with special safety circuits. Based upon the estimates received from the supplier, the system will save 30% of the lighting energy costs, 50% of the lamp replacement cost and all of the present ballast replacement cost. If the cost of the installed system is $15,000.00, what would be the time in months that the investment would pay for itself based upon the following data:*

> *Lighting Energy Cost*
> *Number of fixtures — 445*
> *Average KW per fixture — 0.187*
> *Cost per KWH — $0.085*
> *Annual operating hours — 4,440*
> *Lamp Replacement Cost*
> *Number of fixtures — 445*
> *Average lamps per fixture — 2.25*
> *Average lamp life — 2.5 years*
> *Cost of lamp installed — $6.50*

Ballast Replacement Cost
  Number of fixtures — 445
  Average ballast per fixture — 1.1
  Average ballast life — 4.5 years
  Cost of ballast installed — $40.00

ANSWER: Lighting energy cost = 445 fixtures × 0.187 KW/fixture × 4.440 hrs. × $0.085 = $31,405.34/year

$$\text{Lamp replacement cost} = \frac{445 \text{ fixtures} \times 2.25 \text{ lamps/fx} \times \$6.50}{2.5} = \$2,603.25/\text{yr.}$$

$$\text{Ballast replacement cost} = \frac{445 \text{ fixtures} \times 1.11 \text{ ballasts/fx} \times \$40.00}{4.5} = \$4,351.11$$

Savings estimated if solid state electronic energy conservation system is installed:

$0.30 \times \$31,405.34 = \$\ 9,421.60$
$0.50 \times \$\ 2,603.25 = \ \ \ 1,301.62$
$1.00 \times \$\ 4,351.11 = \ \ \ 4,351.11$
$\qquad\qquad\qquad\text{Total} = \$15,074.33$
$\$15,000.00/15,074.33 \times 12 = 11.94 \text{ months}$

6

Worker and machine relationships

TEXT QUESTIONS

1. *When is it advisable to construct a worker and machine process chart?*

   ANSWER: Any time that it appears that an operator or the machine being operated is non-productive (idle) during a portion of the work cycle.

2. *Why will higher base rates result when machine coupling is practiced?*

   ANSWER: Higher base rates will usually result since the operator is given more responsibility when he/she operates more than one facility.

3. *How does the gang process chart differ from the worker and machine process chart?*

   ANSWER: The gang process chart plots the activity of a group of people servicing one facility or work station, while the worker and machine chart plots the activity of one worker when servicing one or more facilities.

4. *Explain how you would sell machine coupling to union officials strongly opposed to the technique.*

   ANSWER: Point out that higher base rates may result under machine coupling. Also point out that machine coupling has long been accepted practice in many industries such as the textile industry, metal trades in connection with automatic screw machines, and in the plastics industry in connection with the operation of injection molding presses.

5. *In what way does an operator benefit through machine coupling?*

   ANSWER: Higher wages (usually), more responsibility, makes a greater contribution to the company, increases job knowledge (when assigned to two or more different work assignments).

6. *What is the difference between synchronous and random servicing?*

   ANSWER: Synchronous servicing is where both the worker and the machine he or she is servicing are occupied the whole cycle. It is the ideal case which is seldom achieved. Completely random servicing refers to those cases in which it is not known when a facility will need to be serviced or how long servicing will take.

27

7. *How many machines should be assigned to an operator when:*

   a. *Loading and unloading time one machine, 1.41 minutes.*

   b. *Walking time to next facility, 0.08 minutes.*

   c. *Machine time (power feed), 4.34 minutes.*

   d. *Operator rate, $13.20 per hour.*

   e. *Machine rate, $18.00 per hour.*

   ANSWER: $N_1 \leq \dfrac{1 + m}{1 + w} = \dfrac{1.41 + 4.34}{1.41 + 0.08} = 3.859$

   $\therefore$ Let $N_1 = 3$ and $N_2 = 4$

   $\text{T.E.C.}_{N_1} = \dfrac{(1 + m)(K_1 + N_1 K_2)}{N_1} = \dfrac{(5.75)(0.22 + 3 \times 0.30)}{3}$

   $= \$2.147/\text{pc.}$

   $\text{T.E.C.}_{N_2} = (1 + w)(K_1 + N_2 K_2) = (1.49)(0.22 + 4 \times 0.30)$

   $= \$2.116/\text{pc.}$

   $\therefore$ Assign four machines to operator

8. *What proportion of machine time would be lost in operating four machines when the machine operates 70 percent of the time unattended and the operator attention time at irregular intervals averages 30 percent? Is this the best arrangement on the basis of minimizing the proportion of machine time lost?*

   ANSWER: $(p + q)^n = (.70 + .30)^4 =$

   $(.70)^4 + (4)(.70^3)(.30) + \left(\dfrac{4(4\text{-}1)}{2} \right)(.70^2)(.30^2) + \left(\dfrac{4(4 - 1)(4 - 2)}{(3)(2)} \right)(.70)(.30^3) + .30^4$

   $.70^4 = 0.2401$ percentage of time all four machines running

   $(4)(.70^3)(.30) = 0.4116$ percentage of time 3 machines running

   $\dfrac{(4)(4 - 1)}{2} \times (.70^2)(.30^2) = 0.2646$ percentage of time 2 machines running

   $\dfrac{4(4 - 1)(4 - 2)}{(3)(2)} \times (.70)(.30^3) = .0756$ percentage of time 1 machine running

   $.30^4 = .0081 =$ percentage of time 0 machine running

   Total $= 1.000$

No, this would not be the best arrangement if we want to minimize interference time. If we assigned but two machines to the operator then only .09(.30 × .30) of the time would both machines be down; and since the operator could service but one of these down machines, the interference time lost would be only .09 hrs./hr.

9. *In an assembly process involving six distinct operations, it is necessary to produce 250 units per eight-hour day. The measured times are as follows:*

1 — 7.56 minutes	*4 — 1.58 minutes*
2 — 4.25 minutes	*5 — 3.72 minutes*
3 — 12.11 minutes	*6 — 8.44 minutes*

How many operators would be required at 80 percent efficiency?
How many operators will be utilized at each of the six operations?

ANSWER: $\sum\limits_{1}^{6}$ S.M. = 37.66 minutes

$$N = \frac{250}{480} \times \frac{37.66}{.80} = 24.52 \text{ operators}$$

$$= 25 \text{ operators}$$

Will need one unit of production every $\dfrac{480}{250}$ = 1.92 minutes

	Std. Min.	Std. Min./Min. per unit	No. of Operators
Operation 1	7.56	3.94	4
Operation 2	4.25	2.21	3
Operation 3	12.11	6.31	7
Operation 4	1.58	.82	1
Operation 5	3.72	1.94	2
Operation 6	8.44	4.40	5
		Total	22

Since we planned for only 80 percent efficiency, we can use the remaining 3 operators to pick up the slack in the line as relief operators.

GENERAL QUESTIONS

1. *In the process-type plant, which of the following process charts has the greatest application: worker and machine, gang, operation, flow? Why?*

   ANSWER: Probably the flow chart since it highlights distances traveled and delays. These hidden costs are usually prevalent in the process-type plant. Of course, with like machines located together, there is often the opportunity for machine coupling, which is based on the worker and machine process chart.

2. *In the operation of some plant with which you are familiar, outline the "zoning restraints" and discuss how these influence the production line work assignment problem.*

   ANSWER: A zoning restraint represents a subdivision which may or may not be physically separated or identified from other zones in the system. Often it is necessary to confine certain work elements to a given zone. For example, certain work elements may have to be performed within a fire-proof wall according to state law. The more zoning restraints involved in producing a part, the fewer the combinational possibilities open to investigation. Students with work experience should be able to provide several examples.

PROBLEMS

1. *In the Dorben Company's automatic screw machine department, five machines are assigned to each operator. On a given job, the machining time per piece is 0.164 hours. The machining serving time is 0.038 hours, and the average machine downtime is 0.12 hours per machine per hour. With an operator hourly rate of \$12.80 per hour and a machine rate of \$14.00 per hour, calculate the expected cost per unit of output. Exclude material cost.*

   ANSWER: T.E.C. $= \dfrac{K_1 + NK_2}{\text{Pieces from N machines per hour}}$

   Time required to produce one piece/machine $= \dfrac{0.164 + 0.038}{0.88} = 0.23$ hr.

29

Five machines would produce: $5 \times \dfrac{1}{0.23} = 21.74$ pcs./hr.

Expected cost/unit of output: $\dfrac{\$12.80 + 5 \times \$14.00}{21.74} = \$3.809$

2. *In the Dorben Company, an operator was assigned to operate three like facilities. Each of these facilities is down at random times during the day. A work sampling study indicated that on the average the machines operate 60 percent of the time unattended. Operator attention time at irregular intervals averages 40 percent. This arrangement results in the loss of about 14 percent of the available machine time due to machine interference. If the machine rate is $20.00 per hour and the operator rate is $12.00 per hour, what would be the most favorable number of machines (from an economic standpoint) that should be operated by one operator?*

   ANSWER: Expand the binominal $(p + q)^n$ where the operator operates but two machines:
   $(0.60 + 0.40)^2 = 0.36 + 0.48 + 0.16$

   Under this arrangement, the only lost machine time per day would be:
   8 hours $\times$ 1 machine $\times$ 0.16 = 1.2 hours

   and 1.28 hours/2 machines $\times$ 8 hours = 8%

   The savings in machine time, due to interference, with two machine operation would be 14 percent $-$ 8 percent = 6 percent. However, if only two machines were assigned, we would need to employ the equivalent of another one-half an operator at an added cost of $6.00/hr. This would not be justified with only a 6 percent savings of machine time.

3. *The analyst in the Dorben Company wishes to assign a number of like facilities to an operator based upon minimizing the cost per unit of output. A detailed study of the facilities revealed the following:*

   Loading machine standard time = 0.34 minutes

   Unloading machine standard time = 0.26 minutes

   Walk time between two machines = 0.06 minutes

   Operator rate = $12.00 per hour

   Machine rate both idle and working = $18.00 per hour

   Power feed time = 1.48 minutes

   How many of these machines should be assigned to each operator?

   ANSWER: $= \dfrac{.34 + .26 + 1.48}{.34 + .26 + .06} = \dfrac{2.08}{.66} = 3.15$

   $\therefore N_1 = 3$ and $N_2 = 4$

   $K_1 = \dfrac{\$12.00}{60} = \$0.20/\text{min}; \quad K_2 = \dfrac{\$18.00}{60} = \$0.30/\text{min.}$

   $\text{T.E.C.}_{N_1} = \dfrac{(1 + m)(K_1 + N_1K_2)}{N_1} = \dfrac{(0.60 + 1.48)(0.20 + 3 \times 0.30)}{3}$

   $= \$0.763$ per pc.

   $\text{T.E.C.}_{N_2} = (1 + w)(K_1 + N_2K_2) = (0.60 + 0.06)(0.20 + 4 \times 0.30)$

   $= \$0.924$ per pc.

   Therefore assign three machines to the operator.

4. *A work sampling study revealed that a group of three semiautomatic machines assigned to one operator operate 70 percent of the time unattended. Operation attention time at irregular intervals averages 30 percent of the time on these three machines. What would be the estimated machine hours lost per eight-hour day because of lack of an operator?*

ANSWER: $(.70 + .30)^3 = (.70)^3 + (3)(0.70)^2(.30) + (3)(0.70)(0.30)^2 + (.30)^3 = .343 + .441 + .189 + .027$

No. of mch. down	Probability	Mch. hrs. lost/8 hr. day
0	0.343	0
1	0.441	0
2	0.189	(.189)(8) = 1.512
3	0.027	(2)(0.027)(8) .432
	1.000	1.944

1.944 hrs. lost per day because of interference.

7

Motion study

TEXT QUESTIONS

1. *Explain why a bar switch may be preferable to a trigger switch.*

   ANSWER: Engaging or disengaging either of these switches is done with the use of finger motions which are the weakest of the five motion classes. Continuous application of forces results in fatigue and loss of finger flexibility. Bar switches usually require less force application than trigger switches.

2. *Explain why work station designs should endeavor to have the operator perform work elements without having to lift his/her elbows.*

   ANSWER: This procedure can reduce static loading of shoulder muscles, thus reducing fatigue.

3. *What range of height would you recommend for a footrest at a seated workplace?*

   ANSWER: One to nine inches (based upon Figure 7-7).

4. *What seven principles should be employed in connection with work stations where heavy lifting is performed at random intervals?*

   ANSWER: 1. Containers should be designed with handles and to provide load flexibility.

   2. Floors should have adequate friction so as to avoid slippage.

   3. Load should be compact.

   4. Operators should not be required to lift higher than shoulder height.

   5. Operators should be trained to keep loads close to the body and use smooth two-handed symmetrical lifting motions.

   6. Loads over 100 pounds should be considered hazardous.

   7. Movement of loads can be made easier by adjusting the terminal point and access point so that both of these points are near belt level height.

5. *What viewing distance would you recommend for a seated operator working at a computer terminal?*

   ANSWER: 20 inches (based on Figure 7-10).

33

6. *When is visual motion study practical?*

ANSWER: Almost all the time, since the activity of the work need not be large to justify its use economically. It is only when the quantity to be produced is very small that it would not be used in connection with method improvement. However, it would always have application when planning new work stations.

7. *Define and give examples of the 17 fundamental motions or therbligs.*

ANSWER: This is covered in detail beginning on page 166 and ending on page 173.

8. *How may the basic motion "search" be eliminated from the work cycle?*

ANSWER: By providing fixed locations for all tools and work components used by the operator at the work station.

9. *What basic motion generally precedes "reach"?*

ANSWER: Release.

10. *What three variables affect the time for the basic motion "move"?*

ANSWER: Distance, type of move, and the weight being moved.

11. *How does the analyst or observer determine when the operator is performing the element "inspect"?*

ANSWER: When the operator is comparing some object with a standard. The eyes of the operator will focus upon the object while the mind makes a decision to accept or reject.

12. *Explain the difference between avoidable and unavoidable delays.*

ANSWER: An avoidable delay takes place only when the operator is solely responsible, while an unavoidable delay is an interruption beyond the control of an operator.

13. *Why should fixed locations be provided at the work station for all tools and materials?*

ANSWER: To eliminate the basic division search and either eliminate or reduce the basic division select.

14. *Which of the five classes of motions is the one most used by industrial workers?*

ANSWER: Although the text does not spell out this answer, it is generally thought that third class motions are most used by industrial workers.

15. *Why is it desirable to have the feet working only when the hands are occupied?*

ANSWER: Since the hands have more manipulative ability and move faster, for most industrial elements they would be used rather than the foot.

16. *Explain the significance of human dimensions.*

ANSWER: It is important that the analyst is aware of human dimensions so that the product as well as the process, including the work station, be designed to best accommodate the individual or individuals associated with the product and the involved processes.

34

17. *What is the approximate number of calories required by the typical operator per day for sedentary activities? For light manual labor? for medium labor? For heavy manual labor?*

ANSWER: The student is referred to page 249 and Table 9-8. From this he or she will be able to estimate as follows:

For sedentary activities $- \dfrac{2 \times 1{,}700}{3} + 2.5 \times 480 = 2{,}333$ cal/day

For light manual labor $- \dfrac{2 \times 1{,}700}{3} + 3 \times 480 = 2{,}573$ cal/day

For medium labor $- \dfrac{2 \times 1{,}700}{3} + 5 \times 480 = 3{,}522$ cal/day

For heavy manual labor $- \dfrac{2 \times 1{,}700}{3} + 7.5 \times 480 = 4{,}733$ cal/day

18. *Outline the principal guidelines in the design of operators' handgrips, handwheels, and knobs.*

ANSWER: *Knobs* $- \frac{1}{2}''$ to $2''$ in diameter. Diameters increase as greater torques are needed.

Crank and handwheels:
(a) Light loads – use radii of $3''$ to $5''$
(b) Medium loads – use radii of $4''$ to $7''$
(c) Heavy loads – use radii of $8''$ to $20''$

GENERAL QUESTIONS

1. *Which of the 17 therbligs are classed as effective, and usually cannot be removed from the work cycle?*

ANSWER: Reach, move, grasp, release, preposition, use, assemble, disassemble.

2. *Take an operation such as dressing out of your daily routine, analyze it through the operator process chart, and try to improve the efficiency of your movements.*

ANSWER: This could be a homework assignment. For a classroom demonstration the instructor could prepare a pegboard with 30 (or more) holes to accommodate 30 pegs. Then demonstrate various methods to fill the pegboard. One side of the pegboard should have all 30 holes chamfered to reduce position time. One set of pegs should also be pointed to reduce position and assembly time. The best method would be to use chamfered board with pointed pegs and an equal supply of pegs on either side of the board to minimize reach and move distances. Two handed assembly should be used.

3. *Explain why effective visual areas are reduced where concentrated attention will be required.*

ANSWER: When concentrated attention is required more eye fixations are needed which results in a narrowing of the visual area.

4. *Why does a broach usually cost more than a reamer to perform the same sizing operation?*

ANSWER: If the student is not familiar with a broach or a reamer, have him examine these tools from some local machine shop. He will then understand the broach is more costly because it will have more cutting edges (teeth) than the reamer.

5. *Explain why the adjustable seat height of a workplace with a footrest should be higher than a seated workplace without a footrest.*

ANSWER: In order to provide ample adjustment in the height of the footrest.

35

PROBLEMS

1. *A given design has fixed costs of $5,000 and variable cost of $15,000 at 100 percent of company capacity that yields total sales of $30,000. How much more of the plant's capacity must be utilized in order to break even if the fixed costs rise to $8,000.*

    ANSWER: A graphic solution follows. Have students give an algebraic solution by calculating the two break-even points from the straight line equations.

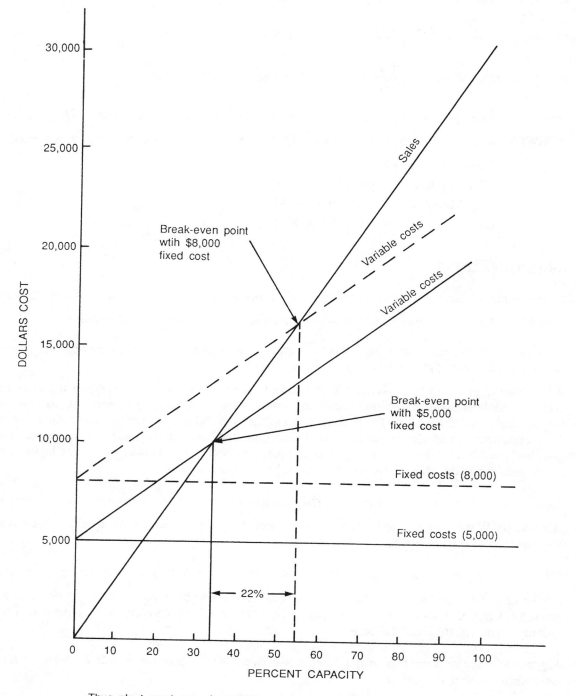

Thus plant must use about 22% more of its capacity in order to break even.

36

2. *Compute the range of work-surface heights that would accommodate all workers through the 98th percentile.*

ANSWER: It is brought out that the work-surface height range to accommodate workers from 1st to 98 percentile is 36.5 to 44.7 inches. From Table A3-2 the first percentile is -1.3σ (approx.) and the 98th percentile is $+2.1\sigma$ (approx.). To cover all people from -3.0σ to $+2.3\sigma$ (99th percentile) would necessitate a work-surface height range of:

$$\frac{44.7 - 36.5}{-(-1.3) + 2.1} = \frac{8.2''}{3.40} \text{ or } \sigma = 2.41 \text{ inches}$$

The low extreme of the work height would equal:

$36.5'' - (3\sigma - 1.3\sigma)(2.41) = 32.4$ inches

The high extreme of the work height would equal:

$44.7 + (2.3\sigma - 2.1\sigma)(2.41) = 45.2$ inches.

Therefore to accommodate all workers through the 98th percentile, seats should be adjustable so table heights would be equivalent to a range of 32.4 inches to 45.2 inches.

3. *What would be the effective visual surface area (in square inches) of an average employee whose work station was centered 26 inches from the center point between his eyes?*

ANSWER: The student is referred to Figure 9-10.

Vertical blanket area $= \dfrac{24 \text{ inches} \times 2 \times \pi \times 125 \text{ degrees}}{360 \text{ degrees}} = 52.36$ inches

Horizontal blanket area $= \dfrac{24 \text{ inches} \times 2 \times \pi \times 156 \text{ degrees}}{360 \text{ degrees}} = 65.35$ inches

Effective visual surface area $= (56.36)(65.35) = 3683$ square inches.

8

Micromotion study

TEXT QUESTIONS

1. *Explain why videotape systems have almost made film systems obsolete.*

   ANSWER: Videotape systems provide high quality moving pictures, even with little light, using relatively inexpensive equipment that is portable, easy to handle and light in weight.

2. *Describe the characteristics of modern videotape systems.*

   ANSWER: Modern videotape systems have a fast (f/1.2) lens allowing pictures to be taken under low light conditions, adjustable electric viewfinder, motordriven zoom lens, diopters allowing the analyst to adjust the eyepiece to his sight, macro setting, instant recorded review capability, automatic iris control, and recording of FM audio signals. They are inexpensive (typically less than $2,000.00 in 1988).

3. *How does micromotion study differ from motion study?*

   ANSWER: Micromotion study is much more detailed than visual motion study. In micromotion study either moving picture film or videotape is employed, while these facilities are not used in visual motion study.

4. *For micromotion study, what additional considerations should be given to "the use of the human body" and "the arrangement and conditions of the workplace"?*

   ANSWER: The best sequences of therbligs should be established; variation in the time required for a given therblig should be investigated; hesitations should be studied and their causes eliminated; cycles and portions of cycles completed in the least amount of time should be used as a goal to attain.

5. *Why is the best operator usually selected in the micromotion procedure?*

   ANSWER: His/her motion pattern is usually superior and he/she invariably is a cooperative employee willing to be filmed.

6. *What consideration should be given the supervisor relative to taking micromotion pictures in his/her department?*

   ANSWER: He/she should be advised several days in advance.

7. *How can micromotion study be helpful in training?*

ANSWER: By making tapes or films of the skilled and trained worker and showing these to untrained workers so that they can pattern their method after the expert.

8. *What are the important steps in making a micromotion study?*

ANSWER: Study the present method and develop a good procedure, select the operator, advise the supervisor and union, take pictures (video or movie), analyze the film through a left and right hand (simo) chart, develop an ideal method, teach the improved method, film and chart the improved method.

9. *How does the simo chart differ from the operator process chart?*

ANSWER: The simo chart is more detailed. The simo chart will chart individual therbligs, while the operator chart plots short elements. The simo chart shows motion classes while the operator chart usually does not.

10. *Which motions are classified as ineffective on the simo chart?*

ANSWER: All but reach, grasp, move, use, and assemble.

11. *What class of motions is signified on the simo chart when plotting a delay?*

ANSWER: First (finger).

12. *What is the purpose of the micromotion instruction sheet?*

ANSWER: To instruct the worker in all details of the recommended method.

13. *In tape or film analysis, why is it inadvisable to analyze both hands simultaneously?*

ANSWER: This would be most difficult because the two hands frequently do not begin or end their therbligs simultaneously.

14. *What advantages does memomotion study have over micromotion study?*

ANSWER: It uses less film or tape and therefore requires less analysis and consequently is much less expensive. Yet it gives adequate detail for work sampling studies, multiworker and multifacility operations.

15. *How much film would be required to study a cycle 13.5 minutes in duration using a memomotion speed of 50 frames per minute?*

ANSWER: $\dfrac{13.5 \text{ min.} \times 50 \text{ frames/min.}}{40 \text{ frames/foot}} = 16.875$ feet.

16. *What filming speed is generally used in making memomotion studies?*

ANSWER: 60 frames/minute.

17. *What range of speeds is possible in memomotion study?*

ANSWER: Two frames/second to one frame every three seconds.

18. *Explain when you would advocate the use of time lapse TV facilities.*

ANSWER: To study long-cycle, multiworker, multifacility type operations. Also it is helpful in studying the flow of several products in connection with plant layout.

GENERAL QUESTIONS

1. *Explain how you would sell the local union steward on the importance of filming only the best two operators when making a micromotion study.*

   ANSWER: Point out that the study is not being made to develop a standard but is being conducted to develop an ideal method that will require less physical and mental effort. The good worker being filmed usually has a good motion sequence.

2. *Make a sketch of your desk or work station and show an arrangement and conditions that would agree with the principles of motion economy and their corollaries.*

   ANSWER: This is a good exercise and the student should incorporate fixed locations for his hand held calculator, pencil, drawing instruments, paper, etc.

3. *Interview at least two factory workers and get their reaction to micromotion study through the film analysis technique.*

   ANSWER: The chances are the student will have to explain to the worker what micromotion study is. The results of this questioning will provide interesting discussion in the classroom.

4. *What activity within an industrial organization other than methods analysis might include the use of micromotion equipment? How?*

   ANSWER: Industrial relations. The filming or taping of various employees is always well received at company picnics, parties, etc.

5. *Discuss the relative merits of the telephoto lens and the wide angle lens.*

   ANSWER: The telephoto will give details of the finger and hand motions (1st and 2nd class). The wide angle will give details of hand, forearm, and upper arm motions (3rd and 4th class).

6. *Why do unions require permission before motion pictures are taken on the production floor?*

   ANSWER: To help protect the personal rights of their members. Not all people want to be photographed.

7. *Compare the cost and quality characteristics of the following compact video systems: Canon, GE, RCA, Sharpe, and Sony. (You will have to acquire this information from your local outlet stores.)*

   ANSWER: The student is urged to become familiar with videotape equipment since these facilities are becoming the most important tool of the methods and work measurement analyst.

8. *In general, what is the operator's attitude toward being filmed?*

   ANSWER: Most people are self-centered enough to want to be photographed and filmed.

9. *How can industrial relations be improved by micromotion studies?*

   ANSWER: By showing the films (permission must be obtained from the employee) at company activities.

10. *Explain what impact, if any, today's philosophy of throwaway type designs has on the use and application of micromotion study.*

    ANSWER: One argument that might be developed is that throwaway designs are usually synonymous with mass, low-cost production where micromotion study has significant application. On the other hand throwaway designs tend to breed an attitude of little concern of small costs which does not dovetail with micromotion philosophy.

11. *What influence does international competition have on the application of micromotion study?*

ANSWER: International competition will drive prices down, thus necessitating more micromotion study.

PROBLEM

In the assembly of small tube-type flashlights in the XYZ Company, two size C (2.5 cm diameter by 4.5 cm length) batteries provide the power. A breakdown of the work elements at each of the 10 assembly stations was as follows:

(a) Reach 44 cm with left hand and pick up tube-type housing.

(b) Simultaneously with (a) reach 50 cm with right hand and pick up two size C batteries.

(c) Palm one battery and assemble one battery in housing. Place second battery in housing.

(d) Reach 40 cm and pick up assembled head. Screw assembled head onto tube-type housing.

(e) Reach 40 cm and pick up spring-loaded end. Assemble end to tube-type housing.

(f) Place assembled flashlight in cardboard carton with left hand. This move averages 50 cm.

Design an improved work station based upon the principles of motion economy. Estimate the hourly savings of your improvement layout if 10 million flashlights are produced.

ANSWER: The improved method should let both hands pick up simultaneously two assembled heads which would be held in a dual fixture. The operator would next pick up (one with each hand) two tube-type housings. Both housings would be simultaneously screwed onto the assembled heads. Next, two batteries would be picked up (one with each hand) and assembled in the two tube-type housings. This operation would be repeated since two batteries are contained in each housing. Now two spring loaded ends would be picked up (one with each hand) and assembled to the housings. Then the two assembled flash lights would be picked up simultaneously (one with each hand) and be deposited into separate cardboard cartons. All reach and move distances should be shortened so that they take place in the normal work area. Gravity feed should be employed so that all materials, in their separate bins, are brought to the normal work area. The fixture may or may not involve power rotation to facilitate the screwing on of the head and spring- loaded end to the housing.

Each student should design his own work station and should provide details as to dimensions and assembly method.

9

Human factors considerations

TEXT QUESTIONS

1. *What are the principal objectives of operation analysis, motion study, and micromotion study?*

    ANSWER: To optimize physical work. To minimize the time required to perform tasks. To maximize the product quality per dollar of cost. To maximize the welfare of the employee from the standpoint of earnings, job security, health, and comfort. To maximize the profit of the business or enterprise.

2. *What areas of study relate to the human factors approach toward improvements?*

    ANSWER: The physical environment of the work station and physiological and psychological factors relating to both the operator and the work force.

3. *What two factors are of concern to the method analyst in connection with artificial lighting?*

    ANSWER: Efficiency (lm/w) and color rendering.

4. *Explain the color rendering effect of low pressure sodium lamps.*

    ANSWER: These light sources have fair to poor color rendering characteristics and probably would not be suitable where color discrimination is necessary as in certain inspection operations.

5. *Would you advocate background music at the work station? What results would you anticipate?*

    ANSWER: Yes, in those production, maintenance, shipping, and receiving operations where analytical activity is not required. It is anticipated that the employees would enjoy the background music and would ask for its continuance if stopped.

6. *Explain what is meant by the "thermal comfort zone."*

    ANSWER: It represents the dry bulb temperature and humidity combinations that are comfortable for most people doing sedentary or light work. The dry bulb temperature range is from 66°F to 79°F and relative humidities range from 20 to 85 percent.

7. *What independent factors affect the quantity of light that is needed to perform a task satisfactorily?*

    ANSWER: The contrast between the object being viewed and the immediate surroundings. The reflectivity of the immediate surroundings. The physical dimensions of the object being viewed. The viewing distance. The time permitted for seeing.

8. *What is the relationship between contrast and seeing time?*

ANSWER: Contrast can be thought of as brightness differences and may be expressed as a percent where:

$$C = \frac{B_L - B_D}{B_L} \times 100$$

With greater contrast the seeing time is diminished.

9. *What footcandle intensity would you recommend 30 inches above the floor in the company washroom?*

ANSWER: Based on Table 9-4, this area would probably be classed as ordinary seeing tasks with a footcandle requirement of approximately 30.

10. *Explain how sales may be influenced by colors.*

ANSWER: It has been proven that color will have psychological effects on people. For example, yellow is the accepted color of butter; therefore margarine must be made yellow.

11. *Would the combined colors of yellow and blue give a harmonious hue? Explain.*

ANSWER: No, because yellow and blue are not adjacent to each other on the color wheel based on the Munsell color system. However, since these colors are approximately opposite to each other they can be considered to be complementary. See Figure 9-2.

12. *What color has the highest visibility?*

ANSWER: Yellow.

13. *How is sound energy dissipated in viscoelastic materials?*

ANSWER: As viscous friction.

14. *A frequency of 2000 Hz would have approximately what wave length in meters?*

ANSWER: Approximately 0.16 meters. (See Figure 9-3)

15. *What would be the approximate decibel value of a grinder being used to grind a high-carbon steel?*

ANSWER: 100 (very annoying) (from Figure 9-4).

16. *Distinguish between broadband noise and meaningful noise.*

ANSWER: Broadband noise is made up of frequencies covering a significant part of sound spectrum; it can be both continuous and intermittent. Meaningful noise represents distracting sound that will have an impact on the worker's efficiency but not on his hearing loss.

17. *According to the present OSHA law, how many continuous hours per day of a 100 dbA sound level would be permissible?*

ANSWER: Two hours (from Table 9-7).

18. *What three classifications have been identified from the standpoint of exposure to vibration?*

ANSWER: Where the major portion of the body surface is affected, where vibrations are transmitted to the body through a supporting area, where vibrations are applied to a localized body area.

19. *In what ways can the worker be protected from vibration?*

    ANSWER: Through the introduction of supports to cushion the body and damp higher amplitude vibrations, alteration of the worker body position so as to lessen the disturbing vibratory forces, reduction of the applied forces responsible for initiating the vibration.

20. *What is meant by the environmental temperature? The effective temperature? The operative temperature?*

    ANSWER: The environmental temperature is the temperature actually experienced by the individual in the environment. The effective temperature is an experimentally determined index based upon the temperature, air movement, and humidity. The operative temperature is the individual's body temperature.

21. *What is the maximum rise in body temperature that the analyst should allow?*

    ANSWER: 1°C or 2°F.

22. *How would you go about estimating the maximum length of time that a worker should be exposed to a particular heat environment?*

    ANSWER: It would be necessary to estimate or measure the heat load. Measurements can be made upon both the environment and the person. On the worker we can measure the heart rate, oxygen consumption and body temperature. The environment measures include the dry-bulb temperature, humidity, air velocity, and radiation from the immediate surroundings.

23. *With a dry-bulb temperature of 80°F, a wet-bulb temperature of 70°F, and an air velocity of 200 feet per minute, what would be the normal effective temperature?*

    ANSWER: 73° (solved graphically from Figure 9-8).

24. *What type of radiation is given the most attention by the safety engineer?*

    ANSWER: Gamma ray, x-ray, and neutron radiation.

25. *What is meant by absorbed dose of radiation? What is the unit of absorbed dose?*

    ANSWER: Absorbed dose is the amount of energy imparted by ionizing radiation to a given mass of material. The unit is the rad.

26. *What is meant by the rem?*

    ANSWER: The unit of dose equivalent is the rem, which produces a biological effect the same as that of one rad of absorbed dose of x or gamma radiation.

27. *What insulation would be required for a stenographic pool of female operators if the ambient temperature were 40°F?*

    ANSWER: Approximately 2.5 clo (from Figure 9-9).

28. *What three factors influence the accuracy of control movements?*

    ANSWER: The number of muscle fibers controlled by each motor nerve ending, the position of the body members, neural stimuli.

29. *What caloric intake would you recommend for an operator doing heavy work? Explain.*

    ANSWER: Assuming his energy expenditure from Table 9-9 is 7.5 calories per minute, he would expend over an eight-hour day: (480)(7.5) = 3,600 calories. This figure plus 1,700 (basal metabolic rate) = 5,300 calories approximately per day.

45

30. *Explain the preferential order of needs that applies to most workers.*

    ANSWER: Basic necessities of life, security, need for belonging to a group, need for status, need for personal self-actualization.

31. *What color would you paint a container used for holding radioactive materials?*

    ANSWER: Purple (see Table 9-11).

GENERAL QUESTIONS

1. *What steps would you take to increase the amount of light in an assembly department by about 15 percent? The department currently uses fluorescent fixtures, and the walls and ceiling are painted a medium green. The assembly benches are dark brown.*

   ANSWER: By repainting the walls and ceiling with a light buff or light yellow paint, the percent of reflected light would be increased from 52 to 70 or approximately 18 percent. The assembly benches could be repainted a light gray or cream where the reflected light would be increased from 10 to 75 percent. The fluorescent fixtures should be cleaned regularly. With the above changes the light should be increased by at least 15 percent. (See Table 9-1.)

2. *What color combination would you use to attract attention to a new product being displayed?*

   ANSWER: Yellow and black. This combination has the highest visibility (see Table 9-6). Yellow tends to instill a feeling of freshness. Also can give the sensation of glory and wealth.

3. *What is the relationship between heartbeat and oxygen consumption?*

   ANSWER: A direct relationship. As the heart beats faster because of greater energy expenditure the oxygen consumption per minute too will increase.

4. *When would you advocate that the company purchase aluminized clothing?*

   ANSWER: When workers need to get exceptionally close to a source of radiant heat.

5. *Are there any possible health hazards in conjunction with electron beam machining? With laser beam machining? Explain.*

   ANSWER: Have your students investigate these two important manufacturing processes. They will find out that the laser beam is a very concentrated monochromatic beam of extremely high intensity. In working with the laser beam care must be exercised so that the eyes are not exposed to this high intensity light.

   The heat generated in electron beam machining is derived from the impingement of a stream of high-velocity electrons on the area where metal is to be removed. As in laser machining, there is great concentration of energy in the beam. Normal precautions are required in electron-beam machining where the process usually requires a vacuum. The precautions for protecting the eyes as in laser machining are not required in electron beam machining.

6. *Explain why supine lifting permits heavier lifts than does prone lifting.*

   ANSWER: In supine lifting, the load is centered over the open hands which provide positive support. With prone lifting, the load is centered over the last joint of the fingers, thus causing the fingers to be pulled open.

7. *Explain why the effective visual areas for average employees is greater for the right eye than for the left eye.*

   ANSWER: Have the students investigate this question with a human factors engineer. The right hand (in right-handed people) has a faster response time and the effective visual area is usually larger (see Figure 9-9). Some theoretical explanations do exist.

8. *Is there a satisfactory explanation for the deterioration of dynamic memory with age?*

ANSWER: Have the students investigate this question with a human factors engineer. There are several theoretical explanations as to why short term memory declines with age.

9. *Explain the impact of noise levels below 85 dbA on office work.*

ANSWER: Most of us have experienced the distraction caused by low office noises making it difficult to concentrate. These noises should be eliminated in those working areas such as design, research, development, and engineering where such distractions will result in low productivity.

PROBLEMS

1. *A work area has a reflectivity of 60 percent, based upon the color combinations of the work stations and the immediate environment. The seeing task of the assembly work could be classified as difficult. What would be your recommended illumination?*

ANSWER: Refer to Table 9-3. For the category of difficult seeing and 50% reflectance we find a footcandle range of 84 to 240 and for 90% reflectance a range of 45 to 153. Therefore for 60% reflectance by interpolation we can estimate:

$$\frac{84 - 45}{4} = 9.75 \text{ and } \frac{240 - 153}{4} = 21.75$$

84 − 9.75 = 74 (approx.) and 240 − 21.75 = 218 (approx.)

Range would be 74 to 218 footcandles.

2. *What would be the level of two uncorrelated noise signals of 86 and 96 decibels?*

ANSWER: Refer to Figure 9-5. The difference in decibel noise signal is 96 − 86 = 10 db. The 10 db line intersects the curved line at .5 db on the vertical scale. The total value is 96 + 0.5 = 96.5 db.

3. *Instructor should note this problem was assigned at end of Chapter 5.*

In the XYZ Company, the industrial engineer designed a work station where the seeing task was difficult because of the size of the components going into the assembly. He established the brightness desired was 100 footlamberts on the average, with a standard deviation of 10 footlamberts so as to accommodate 95 percent of the workers. The work station was painted a medium green having a reflectance of 50 percent. What illumination in footlamberts would be required at this work station in order to provide adequate illumination for 95 percent of the workers? Estimate what the required illumination would be if you repainted the work station with a light cream paint.

ANSWER: Refer to Tables 9-3 and 9-1. Note that for difficult seeing the brightness in footlamberts is 42 to 100. With 50% reflectance we show a footcandle range of 84-240. If we accommodate 95% of workers with a standard deviation of 10 footlamberts we would need a brightness value of 120 footlamberts [100 + (2)(10)]. With 50% reflectance and 120 footlamberts we find a recommended value of 240 footcandles.

With a light cream paint the reflected light would be 75 percent. By interpolation we get:

$$\left(\frac{25}{40}\right) (240 - 133) = 83$$

240 − 83 = 157 footlamberts

4. *Instructor should note that this same problem was given at end of Chapter 5.*

   In the XYZ Company, the industrial engineer was assigned the task of altering the work methods in the press department in order to meet OSHA standards relative to permissible noise exposures. He found that the sound level averaged 100 dbA and that the standard deviation was 10 dbA. The 20 operators in the department were provided with earplugs. Also the power output from the public-address system was altered from 30 watts to 20 watts. The deadening of the sound level of the earplugs was estimated to be 20 percent effective. What improvement resulted? Do you feel that this department is now in compliance with the law at the 99% confidence level? Explain.

   ANSWER: Decibel loss $= 10 \log \frac{P_A}{P_B} = 10 \log \frac{30}{20} = 1.76$

   $$\bar{x}_{dbA} = 100$$

   $$\pm 3\sigma_{dbA} = \pm 30 \text{ dbA}; \text{ range} = 70 \text{ to } 130 \text{ dbA}$$

   With power output modification: 68.24 to 128.24 dbA

   With ear plugs at 3σ limits $= 128.24 - .2 (128.24) = 103$

   $\therefore$ About 2% of time sound level is 103

   About 13% of time sound level is: $120 - 1.76 - .2 (118.24) = 118.24 - 23.65 = 94.59$

   $\therefore$ 2% of 480 $= < 0.5$ hr. $+ 13\%$ of 480 $= 1$hr. approx.

   Based on Table 9-7 this company now is in compliance.

5. *In the XYZ mill room, an all-day study revealed the following noise pollution: 0.5 hrs. 105 dbA; 1 hr. less than 80 dbA; 3.5 hrs. 90 dbA; 2 hrs. 92 dbA; 1 hr. 96 dbA. Is this company in compliance? Explain.*

   ANSWER: From Table 9-7, if: $C_1 T_1 + C_2 T_2 + C_3 T_3 \ldots C_n T_n$ exceeds unity then the mixed exposure is considered to exceed the limit value.

   $\frac{0.5}{1} + 0 + \frac{3.5}{8} + \frac{2}{6} + \frac{1}{3.5} = 0.5 + 0 + 0.4375 + 0.3333 + 0.2857 = 1.5565$ exceeds unity, therefore noise level can be considered excessive.

10

Presentation and installation of the proposed method

TEXT QUESTIONS

1. *What are some of the communication skills that are important in selling a new method?*

   ANSWER: Introducing the idea into the other person's mind, so that he feels it is really his idea. Do not appear overly anxious to have your idea accepted. Present objections and weak points of your own idea.

2. *What are the principal elements of a well-written report?*

   ANSWER: Title page, table of contents, letter of transmittal, summary, body, appendix.

3. *What is meant by the "cash flow" appraisal technique?*

   ANSWER: This method introduces the rate of flow of money in and through the company and the time value of money. It computes the rate of the present worth of cash flow, based upon a desired percentage return, to the original investment.

4. *What are the principal concerns of management with regard to a new method that is relatively costly to install?*

   ANSWER: Estimated savings and the recovery of capital expenditures.

GENERAL QUESTIONS

1. *What is the relationship between return on capital investment and the risk associated with the anticipated sales of the product for which a new method will be used?*

   ANSWER: The greater the risk the larger the value of return on capital investment (i).

   This would be a good time to review some basic engineering economy concepts with the class including the time value of money and depreciation.

2. *When do you feel that the oral report would be more important than the written report in getting approval for a new method?*

   ANSWER: When the methods analyst is especially capable in making an oral presentation and/or when management requests an oral presentation. It usually is more difficult for a manager to turn down a well prepared oral presentation than a written presentation. During the oral presentation the analyst can counter objections to the new method brought out by management.

PROBLEMS

1. *How much capital could be invested in a new method if it is estimated that $5,000 would be saved the first year, $10,000 the second year, and $3,000 the third year? Management expects a 30 percent return on invested capital.*

   ANSWER: $\dfrac{5{,}000}{(1 + 0.30)^1} + \dfrac{10{,}000}{(1 + 0.30)^2} + \dfrac{3{,}000}{(1 + 0.30)^3} = 3{,}846 + 5{,}917 + 1{,}365 = \$11{,}128$

2. *You have estimated the life of your design to be three years. You expect that a capital investment of $20,000 will be required to get it into production. You also estimate, based upon sales forecasts, that the design will result in an after-tax profit of $12,000 the first year and $16,000 the second year, and a $5,000 loss the third year. Management has asked for an 18 percent return on capital investment. Should we go ahead with the investment to produce the new design? Explain.*

   ANSWER: Present value of anticipated profits:

   $$\frac{12{,}000}{(1 + .18)^1} = 10{,}169$$

   $$\frac{16{,}000}{(1 + .18)^2} = 11{,}490$$

   $$\frac{-5{,}000}{(1 + .18)^3} = \underline{-3{,}043}$$
   $$\$18{,}616$$

   This is less than the $20,000 required to go ahead with the new product. Therefore turn down the proposal.

3. *In the Dorben Company, a certain materials handling operation in the warehouse is being done by hand labor. Annual disbursements for this labor and for certain closely related expenses, as social security, accident insurance, other fringe benefits, are $8,200.00. The methods analyst is considering a proposal to build certain equipment that will reduce this labor cost. The first cost of this equipment will be $15,000.00. It is estimated that the equipment will reduce annual disbursements for labor and labor extras to $3,300.00. Annual payments for power, maintenance, and property taxes and nsurance are estimated to be $400.00, $1,100.00, and $300.00 respectively. It is expected that the need for this particular operation will continue for 10 years and, because the equipment is specially designed for the particular purpose, it will have no salvage value. It is assumed that the annual disbursements for labor, power, maintenance, etc. will be uniform throughout the ten years. The minimum rate of return before income taxes is 10 percent. Based upon annual cost comparison, should the company proceed with the new material handling equipment?*

   ANSWER:

Plan A		Plan B	
Labor & labor extras = $8,200.00		CR = $15,000.00 (crf 10% − 10)	
		= $15,000.00 (0.16275) =	$2,441
		Labor & labor extras =	3,300
		Power =	400
		Maintenance =	1,100
		Property taxes & insurance =	300
Total	$8,200.00		$7,541

   Proceed with Plan B and build the new material handling equipment.

   Note: Capital recovery factor $= R = \dfrac{i(1 + i)^n}{(1 + i)^n - 1}$

   $$= \frac{0.10(1 + 0.10)^{10}}{(1 + 0.10)^{10} - 1} = 0.16275$$

50

11

Making the job analysis and the job evaluation

TEXT QUESTIONS

1. *What are the three basic components of factory cost?*

   ANSWER: Direct material, direct labor, and factory expense or overhead.

2. *Is time a common denominator of labor cost? Why or why not?*

   ANSWER: Yes, time is a common denominator of labor cost. Time multiplied by rate equals the cost of labor.

3. *What is job analysis?*

   ANSWER: A procedure for making a careful appraisal of each job and then recording the details of the work so that it can be evaluated.

4. *What four methods of job evaluation are being practiced in this country today?*

   ANSWER: Classification method, point system, factor comparison method, and ranking method.

5. *Explain in detail how a "point" plan works.*

   ANSWER: Establish and define the basic factors, define the degrees of each factor, establish the points to be accredited to each degree of each factor, prepare a job description of each job, evaluate each job by determining the degree of each factor contained in it, sum the points for each factor to get the total points for the job, and convert the job points into a wage rate.

6. *What factors influence the relative worth of a job?*

   ANSWER: Although frequently others are used, the factors most usually applied include: education, experience, initiative and ingenuity, physical demand, mental and/or visual demand, responsibility for equipment or process, responsibility for material or product, responsibility for safety of others, responsibility for work of others, working conditions, and hazards.

7. *Why are estimates unsatisfactory for determining direct labor time standards?*

   ANSWER: Estimates are usually not accurate or consistent enough to be used with confidence.

8. *What is the weakness of using historical records as a means of establishing standards of performance?*

ANSWER: Historical standards usually are not accurate enough to be used as input data for important decision making. Too often they allow more time than is required since delay time is frequently charged to a particular order that really was not related to that order.

9. *What work measurement techniques will give valid results when undertaken by competent trained analysts?*

ANSWER: Stop watch time study, standard data, fundamental motion data, formulae, and work sampling.

10. *What are the principal benefits of a properly installed job evaluation plan?*

ANSWER: To provide the means for compensating all employees within an organization in proportion to their responsibilities and to the difficulty of their work. It will lead to base pay rates in line with remuneration for similar work in the area. Will improve personnel relations.

11. *Explain why a range of rates rather than just one rate should be established for every labor grade.*

ANSWER: This allows for promotion within a labor grade.

12. *Explain what is meant by total operator performance.*

ANSWER: Total performance refers to quality, quantity, safety, attendance, suggestions, and so on.

GENERAL QUESTIONS

1. *Should cost-of-living increases be given as a percentage of base rates or as a straight hourly increment? Why?*

ANSWER: This is a good question to discuss in detail with the class. A straight hourly increment will, of course, penalize the higher paid employees and in time will significantly diminish the difference between base rates of the various job classes. Ideally there should be both a straight hourly increment and a percentage adjustment in order to maintain a satisfactory relationship between the rates of different jobs.

2. *Why would a consulting firm such as George Fry and Associates undertake a comprehensive survey of job evaluation practices?*

ANSWER: It promotes business for them by pointing out the importance of job evaluation, the need to have installations made by competent people, and the difficulties that may be encountered if a poor installation takes place.

PROBLEMS

1. *A job evaluation plan based upon the point system uses the following factors:*

   (a) Experience: maximum weight 200 points: 5 grades

   (b) Education: maximum weight 100 points: 4 grades

   (c) Effort: maximum weight 100 points: 4 grades

   (d) Responsibility: maximum weight 100 points: 4 grades

   A floor sweeper is rated as 150 points, and this position carries an hourly rate of $6.50. A class 3 milling machine operator is rated as 320 points, which results in a money rate of $10.00 per hour. What grade of experience would be given to a drill press operator with an $8.50 per hour rate and point ratings of grade 2 education, grade 1 effort, and grade 2 responsibility?

ANSWER:

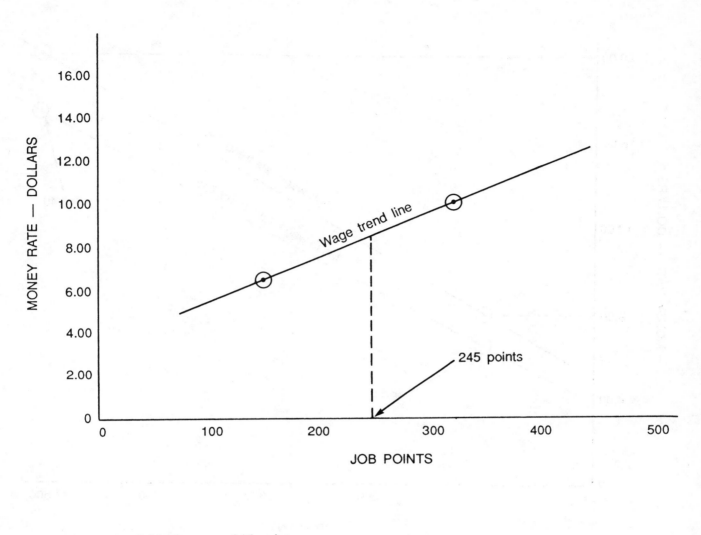

Wage rate of $8.50   = 245 points
Grade 2 education   = 50 points
Grade 1 effort   = 25 points
Grade 2 responsibility   = 50 points
          Total points = 125

245 points − 125 points = 120 points

Therefore, the experience grade = 3

2. *A job evaluation plan in the Dorben Company provides for five labor grades, of which grade 5 has the highest base rate and grade 1 is the lowest. The linear plan involves a range of 50 to 250 points for skill, 15 to 75 points for effort, 20 to 100 points for responsibility, and 15 to 75 points for job conditions. Five degrees are established for each of the four factors. Each labor grade has three money rates: a "low," a "mean," and a "high" rate. If the high money rate of labor grade 1 is $8.00 per hour and the high money rate of labor grade 5 is $20.00 per hour, what would be the mean money rate of labor grade 3? What degree of skill is required for a labor grade of 4 if second degree effort, second degree responsibility and first degree job conditions apply?*

53

ANSWER:

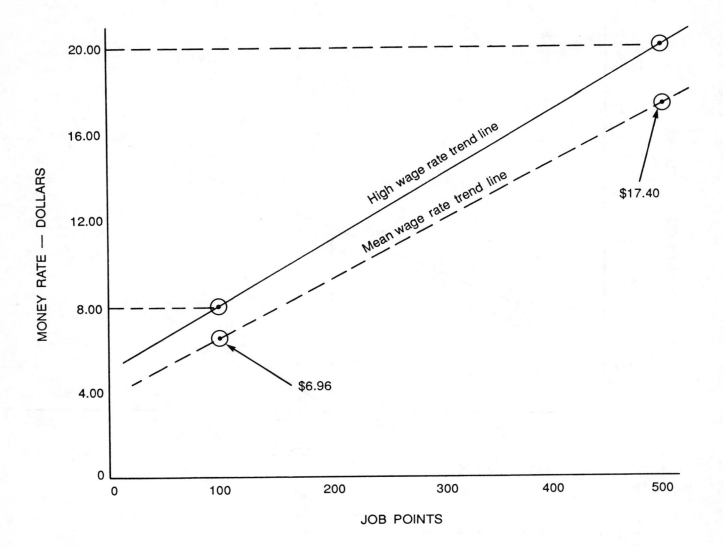

Assuming a plus or minus 15% range for low to high rates within each job class, midpoint of labor grades would be: grade 5 — 500 points, grade 4 — 400 points, grade 3 — 300 points, grade 2 — 200 points and grade 1 — 100 points.

The range of labor grade 4 would be 350 points to 450 points.

2nd degree effort	30 points
2nd degree responsibility	40 points
1st degree job conditions	15 points
Total	85 points

350 − 85 = 265 points

Since maximum skill is 250 points, it is not possible to have a class 4 position with only 2nd degree effort, 2nd degree responsibility and 1st degree job conditions.

54

3. *In the Dorben Company, the analyst has installed a point job evaluation plan covering all indirect employees in the operating divisions of the plant. Ten factors were used in this plan, and each factor was broken up into five degrees. In making the job analysis, the position as shipping and receiving clerk was shown as having 2nd degree initiative and ingenuity valued at 30 points. The total point value of this job was 250 points. The minimum number of points attainable in the plan was 100 and the maximum 500. If ten job classes prevailed, what degree of initiative and ingenuity would be required to elevate the job of shipping and receiving clerk from job class 4 to job class 5? If job class 1 carries a rate of $8.00 per hour and job class 10 carries a rate of $20.00 per hour, what rate does job class 7 carry? (Note rates are based on the midpoint of job class point ranges.)*

ANSWER:

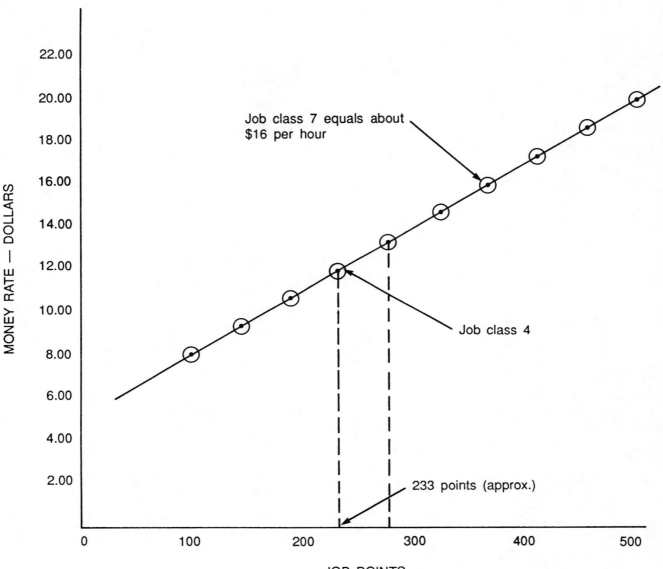

Assume 100 points = $8.00/hr. and 500 points = $20.00/hr.

Then 233 points + 44.4/2 = 255 points, the lower point value of job class 5.

To bring the shipping and receiving clerk up to job class 5, initiative and ingenuity would need to be upgraded from 2nd degree (30 points) to 3rd degree (45 points).

12

Time study requirements

1. *What type of reliability can we expect from estimates?*

   ANSWER: Poor reliability. Standards will be out of line an average of about 25 percent when established by estimates.

2. *How is a fair day's pay determined by the intraplant wage rate inequities agreements of the basic steel industries?*

   ANSWER: Through the application of sound job evaluation.

3. *What benchmark for normal pace is given under these agreements?*

   ANSWER: A man walking without load, on smooth, level ground at a rate of three (3) miles per hour.

4. *Why should the supervisor sign the time study?*

   ANSWER: To indicate that he/she has approved the method being studied and the quality of the operator as to experience, training, and capability to perform the work under study.

5. *Why should the time study person have excellent personal qualities?*

   ANSWER: Because of the nature of time study work. It affects the pocketbook of the worker and the profit and loss statement of the company. Methods work needs the cooperation of the worker as does work measurement in connection with the performance rating procedure.

6. *Explain how poor time standards increase the difficulties of the union steward.*

   ANSWER: Poor time standards mean that some standards are too "tight" and others too "loose." Those operators assigned tight standards will immediately complain to their steward. When the steward has numerous complaints from the workers, problems become magnified.

7. *How can management increase the cooperation of the union steward, the foreman, and the operator in their dealings with the time study analyst?*

   ANSWER: By demonstrating their whole-hearted support for the work measurement effort. By providing training sessions in work measurement where both representatives of labor and management participate.

GENERAL QUESTIONS

1. *Is it customary for the union to cooperate with the time study department to the extent recommended in this text? Is this cooperation likely to occur?*

   ANSWER: This is a good question to have the students investigate with various union officials. They will find out that the cooperation level suggested in this text is seldom realized.

   It can be anticipated that this level will be achieved in the future in those companies that produce products subject to high international competition, such as the automobile and steel industries.

2. *If the requirements for a time study person are so high, why is it that industry does not pay more for time study work?*

   ANSWER: This is another good question that should be assigned to some of the students. When the students consult personnel directors they will find that in many cases the company does not realize the importance of the work measurement effort. There is a tendency to feel the work is less important than other industrial engineering work such as operations research since less mathematical rigor is required in time study work and consequently it is compensated less.

3. *How does the walking pace of three miles per hour agree with your concept of a normal performance?*

   ANSWER: Have the students observe the pace of a person walking at this performance level and get their response to this level of effort. This can easily be done by marking off a distance of 30 feet which should be walked in 6.82 seconds if performing at the three mile per hour pace.

PROBLEM

It has been estimated that the typical plant that has not had the benefits of methods, standards, and wage payment system is operating at about 50 percent of standard. A good methods program should increase productivity to 80 percent of standard. A standards program that is well conceived, operated, and maintained should increase the productivity to 95 percent of standard. And a well-designed and implemented incentive system will further increase productivity to 120 percent of standard.

It has also been estimated that the cost of installing a complete methods, standards, and wage payment system will approximate $30,000 per year for every 100 people coming under the plan.

The XYZ Company employs 650 people. The total value added by production averages 80 percent of the payroll dollar. The average cost of labor (including fringe benefits) is $11.25 per hour. What return on investment can be expected if the XYZ Company installs a complete methods, standards and wage payment system? Show all your calculations.

ANSWER: Company investment: $30,000 × 650/100 = $195,000/yr.

Company annual direct labor cost = 650 × 2,000 hrs. × $11.25 = $14,625,000

Annual total value added by production = 0.80 × $14,625,000 = $11,700,000

$$\frac{0.80 - 0.50}{0.50} \times \$14,625,000 = \$8,775,000 \text{ added productivity by labor through methods.}$$

$$\frac{0.95 - 0.80}{0.50} \times \$14,625,000 = \$4,387,500 \text{ added productivity through standards.}$$

$$\frac{1.20 - 0.95}{0.50} \times \$14,625,000 = \$7,312,500 \text{ added productivity by incentives and good supervision.}$$

Total improvement/yr. = $8,775,000 + $4,387,500 + $7,312,500 = $20,475,000

58

If the work force was paid this total gain (in reality this typically would not happen) then management's gain would be:

$0.80 \times (\$20,475,000 - \$14,625,000) = \$5,850,000$

$\$5,850,000/\$195,000 = 30$ or $30 return for each one dollar invested.

The above assumes there is an inventory of work for the 650 employees at the improved productivity levels. This frequently is not the case and the number of employees will need to be adjusted to meet production requirements.

13

Time study equipment

TEXT QUESTIONS

1. *What equipment is needed by the time study analyst to carry on a program of time study?*

   ANSWER: Minimum equipment includes a good stopwatch or digital electronic watch, a time study board, well designed time study forms, and a pocket calculator such as Texas Instrument (TI) 55 or equivalent.

2. *What features of the decimal minute watch make it attractive to time study analysts?*

   ANSWER: Ease of reading and recording elemental values as they occur. Its simplicity and its accuracy.

3. *Where does the decimal minute watch (0.001 minute) have application?*

   ANSWER: For timing very short elements (less than .04 minute) for standard data development.

4. *How does the duration of one division on the decimal hour watch compare to one division on the decimal minute watch?*

   ANSWER: One division on the decimal hour watch equals: $(60)(0.0001 \text{ hrs}) = 0.0060$ minutes while one division on the decimal minute watch $= 0.010$ min. Therefore one division on the decimal minute watch takes $0.010 \div .006 = 1.667$ times as much time as one division on the decimal hour watch.

5. *Describe in detail the operation of the DataMyte work measurement facility. What advantages does it have over the stopwatch? The electronic timer? What disadvantages?*

   ANSWER: With the DataMyte, the analyst first "keys in" the element number. He then hits "enter" and the DataMyte automatically logs in end-point reading of the element being measured. Subsequently, the inter-faced computer calculates elemental times, average element times, minimum element times, maximum element times, leveling factor times average times, and time allowed. Rating factors and allowances can be keyed in to DataMyte or entered later at the computer keyboard.

   The DataMyte simplifies the work of the analyst and removes the burden of the clerical work that must be done when using the stopwatch or the electronic timer. Errors are minimized and arithmetic errors are eliminated. Studies can be completed in between one-half and two-thirds the time required with the stopwatch or electronic timer. The principal disadvantages with the DataMyte are its cost and the fact that it is somewhat more cumbersome to handle.

6. *What is the principal advantage of the time-recording machine?*

ANSWER: Can be used without the aid of the time study analyst to measure the time that a facility is productive.

7. *What is the memomotion procedure? What are its advantages and limitations?*

ANSWER: The memomotion procedure is a film or videotape analysis procedure where the film or tape is exposed at a much slower speed than is customarily used in motion study. One frame per second is typical of the rate of exposure when conducting a memomotion study.

The principal advantage of memomotion study is that it allows longer cycle filming with minimum exposure of film or videotape and consequently less analysis time. The major disadvantage is that details of specific motions may not be recorded with this technique.

8. *Why is it desirable to provide space for an operator process chart on the time study form?*

ANSWER: This allows the recording of all details of the method being employed by the operator.

9. *Describe the speed indicator and how it is used.*

ANSWER: The speed indicator can be used to give five accurate revolutions of shafting, wheels, and spindles. The instrument has either a contact point or contact wheel which is placed against the work causing the spindle of the instrument to be driven by friction and recording the revolutions per minute of rotating member being measured.

10. *How many feet of film would be exposed on a five-minute cycle while using the memomotion technique?*

ANSWER: Assuming 16 mm. film, there is 40 frames per foot of film. If the memomotion study is taken at one frame per second a five-minute cycle would involve (5)(60) = 300 frames or 300 ÷ 40 = 7.5 feet of 16 mm. film.

11. *How do government specifications of stopwatch equipment compare with the accuracy to which most stopwatches are produced?*

ANSWER: Most stopwatches are produced so as to record time, with accuracies of plus or minus 0.025 minutes over 60 minutes of operation. Government specifications allow a deviation of 0.005 minutes per 30 second inferral. Thus the government permits $(0.005) \left(\dfrac{60 \times 60}{30} \right) = .6$ minute deviation over an hour of operation. Thus most stopwatches on the market today easily meet government specifications.

12. *Explain how a "random elapsed time describer" can be used to train new work measurement analysts.*

ANSWER: It teaches the analyst to use both sight and sound to measure and record successive elements of different duration.

13. *How can the metronome be used as a training tool for performance rating?*

ANSWER: The instructor (operator) can synchronize his pace with the metronome to demonstrate a particular level of performance.

GENERAL QUESTIONS

1. *Explain the statement "The criteria for success are the ability and personality of the time study analyst rather than the equipment he or she chooses to use."*

   ANSWER: The student should understand that the equipment the time study analyst uses is not at all complex. It is both simple and reliable. However, since judgement coupled with sound analysis is necessary in work measurement, the results of this work are almost entirely due to the capability of the individual or individuals performing the work.

2. *Why hasn't industry adopted a standardized time study form?*

   ANSWER: For the same reason industry hasn't adopted a standardized computer language. Different designed forms have unique advantages and disadvantages. Then too the cycle times being measured vary considerably in different industries. A form designed for long cycle measurement would be quite different (in performance rating procedure) from a form designed for short cycle measurement.

3. *Do you feel the typical shopworker would favor the DataMyte facility over the stopwatch? Why or why not?*

   ANSWER: the informed worker should welcome the use of the DataMyte since it is more likely to lead to an error free study. Of course, the student should also be cognizant of everyone's resistance to change. Workers will often object to the use of the DataMyte only because it is new and different from what they are accustomed to seeing.

4. *What would be the advantages using videotape where the features of playback sound as well as operation recorded end points of progressive elements are incorporated?*

   ANSWER: The advantages of employing videotape with recorded sound are important. First, with sound, terminal points of elements are often verified. For example, when a drill breaks through the material being drilled, a characteristic sound is generated that will be picked up by the tape. Then too, the analyst can provide details of foreign elements as they occur, thus justifying the discarding of certain unrealistic elements and determining the extent of extra allowances.

PROBLEMS

1. *In order to demonstrate various levels of performance to a group of union stewards, the time study supervisor of the XYZ Company is using the metronome while dealing bridge hands. How many times per minute should the metronome beat to demonstrate the following levels of performance: 60 percent, 75 percent, 100 percent, 125 percent?*

   ANSWER: 60 percent = .60 × 104 beats = 62 beats/min.
               75 percent = .75 × 104 beats = 78 beats/min.
               100 percent = 1.00 × 104 beats = 104 beats/min.
               125 percent = 1.25 × 104 beats = 130 beats/min.

2. *What would be the synthetic time value to reach 20 inches for a 15-pound casting, move it 15 inches, and place it in a fixture requiring 0.020 minutes position time and a grasp involving 0.004 minutes? See Chapter 19.*

    ANSWER: From Table 19-4

    $$\begin{array}{rl}
    \text{Reach} = \text{RB20} = & 18.6 \text{ TMU} \\
    \text{Move} = \text{MC20} = & 22.1 \text{ TMU} \\
    \text{Release} = \text{RL1} = & \underline{2.0} \text{ TMU} \\
    & 42.7 \text{ TMU} = 0.0256 \text{ min.}
    \end{array}$$

    Position   = .0200 min.
    Grasp   = .0040 min.
    R + M + RL = .0256 min.

    Total synthetic time = 0.0496 minutes.

3. *If government regulations permit an average deviation of 0.005 minutes per 30 second interval and a standard deviation of 0.001, what is the maximum deviation in seconds per minute that would be permitted at the 99 percent confidence level?*

    ANSWER: $\bar{x}$ = 0.005 minutes/30 second interval

    σ = 0.001 minutes/30 second interval

    $\pm$ 3 σ = $\pm$ 0.003 = 0.002 to 0.008/30 second interval

    Maximum deviation per 30 second interval = 0.008 minutes.

14

Elements of time study

TEXT QUESTIONS

1. *Outline the characteristics that the operator should have if he or she is selected for time study.*

   ANSWER: The operator should have a record of being average or better than average in performance and be completely trained in the method to be studied. The operator should possess a liking for the work and have an interest in doing a good job. He/she should have a cooperative spirit.

2. *What are the principal responsibilities of the time study observer?*

   ANSWER: To record all details of the method under study, to evaluate the performance of the operator objectively, to measure all the elements of the job under study precisely, to calculate the standard accurately, and to behave professionally to representatives of both management and labor.

3. *What are some of the qualifications of the successful time study analyst?*

   ANSWER: Analytically sound, good judgement, ability to articulate, good shop knowledge, warm personality, honesty, and enthusiasm.

4. *How does the time study analyst "directly affect the pocketbook of the worker"?*

   ANSWER: The time study analyst establishes the standard. In incentive plans the operator is paid for performance above standard in proportion to output. In day work plants, merit increases in compensation are largely a result of performance above standard.

5. *Explain the statement that all supervisors are "management's representatives throughout the plant."*

   ANSWER: Supervisors have line authority over the workers that they supervise. Management policy is disseminated to employees through the supervisors.

6. *Why do supervisors require fair time standards in their departments?*

   ANSWER: Supervisors are largely responsible for the welfare of their workers. Thus they should do their best to assure that only fair standards are established, Then too, they are usually held responsible for production schedules, which can only be realized if they are based upon fair standards. Cost centers are usually based upon standards. Thus poor standards will result in excessive budget variation.

7. *What are the main responsibilities of the supervisor in relation to time study work?*

   ANSWER: To assure that the method being studied is satisfactory and that the quality and experience of the operator is adequate. He/she should see to it that both the operator and union steward have been notified in advance that a study is to be made.

8. *What is the significance of the supervisor's signature on the time study?*

   ANSWER: This signature indicates his/her approval of the method being used when the study was taken.

9. *What is a fair day's work?*

   ANSWER: A fair day's work is a full day's work, at normal performance. with reasonable allowances for personal delays, unavoidable delays, and fatigue.

10. *Explain how having an appreciation course in the elements of time study made available to all employees will promote good labor relations.*

    ANSWER: When workers and union representatives understand all aspects of the work measurement procedure and the economic necessity of having good standards, they will be much more sympathetic to the efforts of the time study analyst. Consequently most questions and disagreements resulting from standards will be able to be settled by the supervisor in concert with the time study analyst, the worker, and the union steward without the submission of a formal grievance.

11. *What considerations should be given to the choice of the operator to be studied?*

    ANSWER: Always endeavor to select an operator who has a record of performing at normal or somewhat above normal, who is cooperative, dependable and conscientious. He or she should have a favorable attitude to the work measurement procedure and should have an open mind in connection with method improvement.

12. *Of what use is the operator process chart on the time study form?*

    ANSWER: The operator process chart allows the analyst to provide a detailed record of the method under study.

13. *Why is it essential to record complete information on tools and the facility on the time study form?*

    ANSWER: Because the tools and facility being used represent, to a large extent, the method being employed. A standard is established for a specific method and usually is not applicable for alternative methods. Therefore the method for which the standard is being established must be completely identified.

14. *Why are the working conditions important in identifying the method being observed?*

    ANSWER: Because the standard is established for the working conditions that usually prevail at the work center. If these conditions deviate considerably from the usual conditions then the standard may need to be modified.

15. *Why would a time study analyst who is hard of hearing have difficulty in recording his stopwatch readings of terminal points?*

    ANSWER: Because in many cases sound identifies the conclusion of one element (at which time the watch should be read) and the beginning of the next element. An analyst who is hard of hearing would not be consistent in regard to reading the watch at terminal points where a distinct sound occurs.

16. *Differentiate between constant and variable elements. Why should they be kept separate when dividing the job into elements?*

    ANSWER: Constant elements are those elements for which the time will deviate very little within a specified range of work while variable elements are those for which the time will vary within a specified range of work. Constant elements should be kept separate from variables so that the completed study can be used as a source of standard data or formula construction.

17. *Explain how repeating elements may be recorded on the time study form.*

ANSWER: By recording the watch readings of the repeating elements in the same column as the one in which the first occurrence of the element was recorded.

18. *What advantages does the continuous method of watch recording offer over the snapback method?*

ANSWER: It provides a complete record of the entire observation period. It is better adapted to measuring and recording very short elements. No time is lost in snapping the hand back to zero.

19. *Explain why the electronic time study instrument has broadened the use of the snapback procedure.*

ANSWER: With the electronic watch, no time is lost in moving a hand back to zero. Thus, the snapback procedure is useful for the measurement of both short and long elements.

20. *Why is the time of day recorded on the time study form?*

ANSWER: This provides a gross overall check as to whether any arithmetic errors were made in the study. The time of day also helps identify the method under study.

21. *What variations in sequence will the observer occasionally encounter during the course of the time study?*

ANSWER: Observer misses a reading, the operator will occasionally miss an element, at times he may perform elements out of sequence, and from time to time foreign elements will be introduced.

22. *Explain what a foreign element is and how foreign elements are handled under the continuous method.*

ANSWER: A foreign element is one introduced by the operator during the study that was not planned at the time the elements of the study were established.

When a foreign element occurs, the observer will signify the event by an alphabetical designation in the "T" column. A short description of the foreign element is made in the space provided after the corresponding reference letter and it is timed as regular elements.

23. *What factors enter into the determination of the number of cycles to observe?*

ANSWER: Activity of the job, the cycle time of the job, the chance for repeat business, the variation in time of the elements after the first few cycles have been measured.

24. *Why is it necessary to performance rate the operator?*

ANSWER: In order to adjust the time of the good operator up to normal and the time of the poor operator down to normal.

25. *When should individual elements of each cycle be rated?*

ANSWER: When the elemental time is of such length that the analyst will have adequate time to make a good evaluation of the performance as well as measure and record the elapsed time.

26. *Define a "normal" operator.*

ANSWER: See Appendix 1. An operator who can achieve the established standard of performance when following the prescribed method and working at an average pace.

27. *For what reasons are allowances applied to the normal time?*

ANSWER: To take care of personal delays, unavoidable delays, and fatigue so that a fair standard is developed that can be achieved by the normal operator when exerting average effort.

28. *What is the significance of a "circled" elapsed time?*

ANSWER: These values are excluded from further consideration in working up the study.

29. *What steps are taken in the computation of a time study conducted by the continuous overall performance rating procedure?*

ANSWER: (a) Make subtraction of consecutive readings and record.

(b) Circle all abnormal values.

(c) Summarize remaining elemental values.

(d) Calculate the average time of the observed values.

(e) Calculate normal elemental times by multiplying by the performance factor.

(f) Add appropriate allowance to obtain elemental allowed times.

(g) Summarize the elemental allowed times to obtain the standard time.

30. *Based upon the Westinghouse guide sheet, how many observations should be taken on an operation whose annual activity is 750 pieces and whose cycle time is estimated at 15 minutes? What would be the number of observations needed according to the General Electric guide sheet?*

ANSWER: See Table 14–3. Cycle time is over 0.20 hours and activity is under 1,000, therefore take 5 cycles. From Table 14–2 (10.00 − 20.00) = 8 cycles.

31. *You anticipate using the DataMyte for developing some standard data on short cycle elements involved in the use of a 100 ton punch press. You will need to take approximately 1,000 observations. How many K of memory is required?*

ANSWER: The DataMyte is limited to approximately 500 observations per 4 K of memory. An 8 K DataMyte will handle the 1,000 observations required.

GENERAL QUESTIONS

1. *What do you feel the difference is between (a) a normal operator, (b) an average operator, and (c) a standard operator?*

ANSWER: Discuss this question with your students. Usually a normal operator is synonymous with a standard operator. An average operator may be above or below a normal operator in performance. In incentive plants the average operator is usually better thant the normal operator in performance while in the typical day-work operation, the average operator is below the normal operator in performance.

2. *Why are time study procedures the only techniques for supplying reliable information on standard times?*

ANSWER: They are the only techniques based upon measurement and the utilization of a rating factor.

3. *To what positions of importance does time study work lead?*

ANSWER: Discuss this at length with your students and give several examples. Time study work leads to positions in production planning and control, estimating, sales, and managerial positions in line supervision and manufacturing.

4. *In what way can "loose" time standards result in poor labor relations?*

ANSWER: Loose rates will cause considerable dissatisfaction by those employees that have been assigned fair standards. This will result in sufficient controversy so as to cause poor labor relations.

5. *Why are poor time standards a "headache" to union officials?*

ANSWER: The union official wishes to keep the employees content. Poor time standards will cause employees to be discontented and the union officials will have much of this discontent directed toward them.

6. *How would you approach a belligerent operator if you were the time study analyst?*

ANSWER: This question is worth spending some time on. The best approach is in concert with the line supervisor (foreman). The analyst should portray a friendly yet business-like approach. He should take time to respond in detail to all questions posed by the belligerent operator.

7. *You were using the General Electric guide sheet to determine the number of observations to study. It developed that 10 cycles were required, and after taking the study you observed the standard error of the mean statistic to estimate the number of observations needed for a given confidence level. The resulting calculation indicated that 20 cycles should be studied. What would be your procedure? Why?*

ANSWER: Definitely take 20 cycles. The study of 10 more cycles is a small price to pay to assure that an adequate sample of data has been taken.

8. *Based upon the data provided in Figures 14–6 and 14–7, would it be a good idea to have the operator load and unload a second die casting machine? Explain.*

ANSWER: It should be apparent from reviewing this study that the operator should not be assigned a second die casting machine. The standard cycle time is 0.618 min. and the machine cycle time is 0.35 min. With the operator serving but one machine, the idle machine time is considerable. Assigning a second machine would compound the idle machine time and would not be cost effective.

PROBLEMS

1. *What would be the required number of readings if the analyst wanted to be 87 percent confident that the mean observed time was within ± 5 percent of the true mean and she established the following values for an element after observing 20 cycles: 0.09, 0.08, 0.10, 0.12, 0.09, 0.08, 0.09, 0.12, 0.11, 0.12, 0.09, 0.10, 0.12, 0.10, 0.08, 0.09, 0.10, 0.12, 0.09?*

ANSWER: $N = \left(\dfrac{st}{k\bar{x}}\right)^2$

$\bar{x}$ = .09 + .08 + .10 + .12 + .09 + .08 + .09 + .12 + .11 + .12 + .09 + .10 + .12 + .10 + .08 + .09 + .10 + .12 + .09/19 = 0.099

t = 1.61 (See Table A3–3 interpolate for n = 19 and probability = .13)

k = .05

$s = \sqrt{\dfrac{\Sigma(x_1 - \bar{x})^2}{n - 1}} = 0.0143$

$N = \left[\dfrac{(0.0143)(1.61)}{(.05)(0.10)}\right]^2 = 21.1$

Thus 21 cycles should be taken. The 20 cycles observed (note there was one wild value since only 19 values were used for computation) is a reasonably adequate sample of data.

2. *The following data resulted from a time study taken on a horizontal milling machine:*

Pieces produced per cycle: 8
Mean measured cycle time: 8.36 minutes
Mean measured effort time per cycle: 4.62 minutes
Mean rapid traverse time: 0.08 minutes
Mean cutting time (power feed): 3.66 minutes
Performance factor: + 15
Machine allowance (power feed): 10 percent
Effort allowance: 15 percent

An operator works on the job a full eight-hour day and produces 380 pieces.

(a) how many standard hours does the operator earn?
(b) What is his efficiency for the day?
(c) If his base rate is $7 per hour, compute his earnings for the day if he is paid in direct proportion to his output.

ANSWER: Normal effort time = (4.62)(1.15) = 5.313 minutes
Allowed effort time = (5.313)(1.15) = 6.110 minutes
Allowed rapid traverse time = (0.08)(1.00)(1.10) = .088 minutes
Allowed cutting time = (3.66)(1.00)(1.10) = 4.026 minutes
Allowed cycle time = 10.224 minutes
Allowed time/pc. = $\frac{10.224}{8}$ = 1.278 minutes

$\frac{(380)(1.278)}{60}$ = 8.094 standard hrs. earned

$\frac{8.094}{8}$ = 101.175% efficiency

(8.094)($7) = $56.66 earnings for the day.

3. *A work measurement analyst in the Dorben Company took 10 observations of a high-production job. He performance rated each cycle and then computed the mean normal time for each element. The element with the greatest dispersion had a mean of 0.30 minutes and a standard deviation of 0.03 minutes. If it is desirable to have sampled data within ± 5 percent of the true data, how many observations should this time study analyst take of this operation?*

ANSWER: $N = \left(\frac{st}{k\bar{x}}\right)^2 = \left[\frac{(0.03)(2.228)}{(0.5)(.30)}\right]^2$ = 19.86 or 20 cycles

4. *In the Dorben Company, the work measurement analyst took a detailed time study of the making of shell molds. The third element of this study had the greatest variation in time. After studying nine cycles, the analyst computed the mean and standard deviation of this element, with the following results: $\bar{x} = 0.42$ s = 0.08.*

If the analyst wanted to be 90 percent confident that the mean time of his sample was within ± 10 percent of the mean of the population, how many total observations should he have taken? Within what percent of the average of the total population is $\bar{x}$ at the 95 percent confidence level under the measured observations?

ANSWER: $N = \left(\frac{st}{k\bar{x}}\right)^2 = \left[\frac{(0.08)(1.833)}{(.10)(0.42)}\right]^2$ = 12.19 or 12 observations should be taken.

$\bar{x} \pm t\frac{s}{\sqrt{n}}$ = .42 ± (1.833) $\left(\frac{.08}{\sqrt{9}}\right)$
= .42 ± 0.05
= .42 ± 12%

15

Performance rating

TEXT QUESTIONS

1. *Why has industry been unable to develop a universal conception of "normal performance"?*

   ANSWER: Competition will have an impact on the concept of normal performance. With the application of fundamental motion data, MTM and Work Factor for example, there is a trend to a more uniform concept of what normal performance is.

2. *What factors enter into large variances in operator performance?*

   ANSWER: The method used by various operators; operators skill, effort, and experience on the class of work; the operating conditions.

3. *What are the characteristics of a sound rating system?*

   ANSWER: Accuracy, consistency among the various users of the system, simple, concise, easily explained by keying to well established benchmarks.

4. *When should the performance rating procedure be accomplished? Why is this important?*

   ANSWER: Rating should be done during the course of the observation of the elemental times. When rating is done at this time, the operator can be advised of his performance prior to the analyst leaving the work station. It is when the analyst is at the work station that he is able to provide his best judgement of the skill and effort demonstrated.

5. *What governs the frequency of performance rating during a given study?*

   ANSWER: The length of the elements, the length of the cycle time, the number of parts to be produced.

6-7. *Explain the Westinghouse system of leveling. How does the Westinghouse performance rating differ from the leveling method?*

   ANSWER: The original Westinghouse system evaluated skill, effort, conditions and consistency in order to provide a performance factor. The Westinghouse "performance rating plan" considers dexterity, effectiveness, and physical application in order to arrive at a rating factor.

8. *Under the Westinghouse rating system, why are "conditions" evaluated?*

   ANSWER: Because when conditions that affect the operator such as temperature, humidity, etc. are different from what they are customarily found at the work station, performance will be affected.

71

9. *What is synthetic rating? What is its principal weakness?*

ANSWER: A method of rating where a performance factor is determined by timing representative effort elements of the work cycle and comparing these elemental values to time values determined by fundamental motion data for these same elements.

The principal weakness is the time required to make the analysis which would usually be done away from the work station.

The students should also be advised that several research reports have indicated that synthetic leveling with the establishment of a uniform rating factor to be applied to the whole study will frequently give results that could better be obtained by alternative rating methods.

10. *What is the basis of speed rating, and how does this method differ from the Westinghouse system?*

ANSWER: Speed rating gives consideration only to the rate of accomplishment of the work per unit time. Thus it differs from the Westinghouse method which considers the dexterity, effectiveness, and physical application of the worker.

11. *What is the purpose of the "secondary adjustment" in the objective rating technique? What factors are considered in the "secondary adjustment"?*

ANSWER: The secondary factor is assigned to allow for the relative difficulty of the job being performed. The factors considered include: amount of body used, foot pedals, bimanualness, eye-hand coordination, handling or sensory requirements, weight handled or resistance encountered.

12. *What four criteria are fundamental for doing a good job in speed rating?*

ANSWER: (a) Experience on the part of the analyst in the work being performed.
(b) Benchmarks for two (or more) of the elements being performed.
(c) Selection of a satisfactory operator who usually performs between 85% and 115%.
(d) The use of the mean value of three or more independent studies.

13. *Why is training in performance rating a continuous process?*

ANSWER: Because concepts of normal can change in time. As with all activities that require judgement and skill, it is necessary to have continuous practice.

14. *Using the data illustrated in Figure 15–5, determine the average percentage of correct rating within plus or minus 5 rating points.*

ANSWER: From Figure 15–5 the following data has been extracted:

Study No.	Analyst's Rating	Correct Rating	Difference	Difference Squared
1	74	54	+ 20	400
2	78	70	+ 8	64
3	78	84	− 6	36
4	105	100	+ 5	25
5	110	110	0	0
6	135	125	+ 10	100
7	140	150	− 10	100
			+ 27	725

$$\bar{x}_d = \frac{\Sigma d}{n} = \frac{+\ 27}{7} = 3.86$$

$$s_d = \sqrt{\frac{\Sigma d^2 - [(\Sigma d)^2 \div n]}{n - 1}} = 10.2$$

$$Z_1 = \frac{5.00 - 3.86}{10.2} = .11\sigma$$

$$Z_2 = \frac{5.00 - 3.86}{10.2} = -.87\sigma$$

$$.11\sigma = 0.0438$$

$$-.87\sigma = \frac{0.2036}{.2474}$$

Percentage of correct ratings within plus or minus 5 rating points equal 24.74 percent.

15. *Why is performance rating the most important step in the entire work measurement procedure?*

    ANSWER: Because it has a significant impact on the final results and is the only step where judgement on the part of the analyst plays a major role.

16. *Why should more than one element be used in the establishment of a synthetic rating factor?*

    ANSWER: The average of two or more independent ratings will give a more reliable estimate of the correct performance than a single rating.

GENERAL QUESTIONS

1. *Would there be any objection to studying an operator who is performing at an excessive pace? Why or why not?*

    ANSWER: It would be preferable to study an operator who is working at a more normal pace. It is difficult to evaluate accurately performances at either end of the rating scale. Excessive performance tends to be rated too low by the typical analyst and very slow performance tends to be rated too high.

2. *In what ways can an operator give the impression of high effort and yet produce at a mediocre or poor level of performance?*

    ANSWER: She can give the impression of high effort by performing quick movements during the "get" and "put" portions of the work cycle while giving poor performance on the "use" or "do" portions of the cycle. Also by counting to herself so that she utilizes about the same time per cycle, she can give the impression of consistency and high performance.

3. *If an operator strongly objected to his performance rating factor upon completion of the study, what would your next step be if you were the time study analyst?*

    ANSWER: Calculate the standard and have the operator measure the time it takes him to produce a part. He probably will find it is quite easy to achieve the standard and consequently the performance rating should be acceptable to him.

4. *How would you go about maintaining a uniform concept of normal performance in a multiplant enterprise whose various plants are located in different sections of the country?*

    ANSWER: The best way to do this is by the regular exchange of videotapes and/or films demonstrating various levels of performance on different jobs within the plants.

PROBLEMS

1. *In the Dorben Company, 200 units of a new design were produced. The total time required to produce these 200 units was maintained by having all the operators involved "punch in" and "punch out" on this line of work. The total recorded time was 25,412 hours. After 400 units of the new product were produced, it was noted that 42,808 hours had been utilized. From the data recorded, what is the learning curve associated with this new product?*

   ANSWER: $\dfrac{25,412}{200}$ = 127.06 hrs. cumulative average time for 200 units

   $\dfrac{42,808}{400}$ = 107.02 hrs. cumulative average time for 400 units

   $\dfrac{107.02}{127.06}$ = 84% learning curve

2. *The analyst is studying a complete assembly operation that takes place in her plant in conjunction with a new product line. She anticipates that an 85 percent rate of learning will take place. In order to develop helpful learning curve information for future planning, she wishes to compute the rate of learning that takes place on this assembly work. After 50 units were produced, the analyst noted a total assembly time charge of 1,000 work-hours. Only 500 more work-hours were needed to produce an additional 50 units. What learning curve percentage was taking place?*

   ANSWER: $\dfrac{1,000}{50}$ = 20 cumulative average hrs./unit after 50 units

   $\dfrac{1,500}{100}$ = 15 cumulative average hrs./unit after 100 units

   $\dfrac{15}{20}$ = 75 percent

   A 75 percent learning was taking place rather than the anticipated 85 percent.

3. *The work measurement analyst in charge of training time study analysts decided to have all trainees review 20 film loops, where the rate of each loop was known. Each trainee then computed his/her own record, which was based on the proportion of ratings that fell within plus or minus five points of the known ratings.*

   One analyst computed the average difference in rating as −4.08 points on the 20 films. The standard deviation was 6.4. What percentage of this analyst's ratings was contained within the desired rating?

   ANSWER: $\bar{x}_d = -4.08$; $s_d = 6.4$

   $Z_1 = \dfrac{5.00 - (-4.08)}{6.4} = 1.42$ $\sigma = .4472$

   $Z_2 = \dfrac{-5.00 - (-4.08)}{6.4} = 0.14$ $\sigma = \dfrac{.0556}{.5028}$

   50.28 percent contained within the desired rating.

4. *The Dorben Company is using synthetic leveling on its low-skill highly repetitive operations. A time study analyst for the company finds that the mean time required by a given operator for element 2 averages 0.05 minute. An MTM analysis of this element involves the following:*

   One class A 20 inch reach; one class C grasp; one class C 24 inch move; one position involving a semisymmetrical assembly with light pressure and a relatively easy-to-handle part; one normal release.

   What performance factor will be assigned to the effort elements of this study? What would the allowed time for element 2 be if a P.D.&F. allowance of 20 percent were utilized?

ANSWER: R20A   = 13.1
           GICI   =   7.3
           M20C   = 22.1
           P2SSE = 19.7
           RL $-$ 1 = $\underline{2.0}$
                     64.2 T.M.U. = .03852 minutes

$\dfrac{.03852}{.05}$ = 77% performance factor to be assigned.

Allowed time for element 2 equals: $(.05)(.77)(1.2) = .0462$ minutes.

5. *In the Dorben foundry, an order of 20 large castings is being produced. For the first 10 castings, the average time per casting is 40 work-hours. What would the learning curve percentage be if the average time per casting were 35 hours upon completion of the order?*

    ANSWER: 40 hrs. average time per casting for first 10.

               35 hrs. average time per casting for first 20.

               $\dfrac{35}{40}$ = 87.5 percent learning curve.

16

Allowances

TEXT QUESTIONS

1. *Compare the interference delay allowance using the queuing model and Wright's equation where N = 20, mean facility running time is 120 minutes, and attention time is 3 minutes.*

   ANSWER: $k = \dfrac{T_2}{T_1} = \dfrac{3}{120} = 0.025$

   $N = 20$

   Using Table A3–14 (Appendix 3) and interpolating from tables where K = 0.6 and 1.6 for N=20 (using column *a* since we are assuming constant service time) $T_3 = 1.1$

   $\therefore T_3 = .011$ C where C is the cycle time to produce one unit/spindle

   $120 + 3 + .011$ C $= $ C

   $\qquad .989$ C $= 123$

   $\qquad\qquad$ C $= 124.36$ minutes

   $T_3 = (.011)(125.06) = 1.38$ minutes interference

   Wright's model: $I = 50\left[\sqrt{(1 + x - N)^2 + 2N} - (1 + x - N)\right]$

   $\qquad\qquad = 50\left[\sqrt{(1 + {}^{120}\!/_3 - 20)^2 + (2)(20)} - (1 + {}^{120}\!/_3 - 20)\right]$

   $\qquad\qquad = 50\left[\sqrt{481} - (21)\right]$

   $\qquad\qquad = 46.59\%$

   $(.4659)(3) = 1.40$ minutes interference

2. *What three broad areas are allowances intended to cover?*

   ANSWER: Personal delays, fatigue, and unavoidable delays.

3. *To what three categories of the time study are allowances provided? Give several examples of each.*

   ANSWER: Allowances applicable to machine time only such as power variance allowance, allowances applicable to total cycle time such as personal delay allowances, and allowances applicable to effort time only such as fatigue allowances.

4. *What are the two methods used in developing allowance standard data? Briefly explain the application of each technique.*

ANSWER: Production study and work sampling study. The production study finds application where a grievance has been submitted since the entire day (days) will be under the scrutiny of the analyst who will measure the time and cause of all delays encountered. It is used primarily as a verification tool.

The work sampling study is generally used today for the purpose of establishing allowances for various work categories.

5. *Give several examples of personal delays. What percentage allowance seems adequate for personal delays under typical shop conditions?*

ANSWER: Trips to the rest room, drinking fountain, etc. 24 minutes per working day of 8 hours is considered adequate.

6. *What are some of the major factors that affect fatigue?*

ANSWER: Light, temperature, humidity, air freshness, color of room, noise, concentration necessary to perform task, monotony of similar body movements, position employee must assume to perform operation, stress of muscles required, physical stature of employee, diet, rest, home conditions, employee's stability.

7. *Under what groups have the tests of fatigue been classified?*

ANSWER: Physical, chemical, physiological.

8. *What operator interruptions would be covered by the unavoidable delays allowance?*

ANSWER: Interruptions from the supervisor, dispatcher, time study analyst, etc.: material irregularities, interference delays.

9. *What percentage allowance is usually provided for avoidable delays?*

ANSWER: None.

10. *When are extra allowances provided?*

ANSWER: To take care of the additional time resulting from a substandard lot of raw material or temporary working conditions that are poorer than normal. Attention time allowances are frequently added as an extra allowance. This is especially true in the steel industry.

11. *What fatigue allowance should be given to a job if it developed that it took 1.542 minutes to perform the operation at the end of continuous work and but 1.480 minutes at the beginning of continuous work?*

$$\text{ANSWER:} = \frac{(T - t)\ 100}{T}$$

$$= \frac{(1.542 - 1.480)\ 100}{1.542}$$

$$= 4.02\%$$

12. *Why are allowances based on a percentage of the productive time?*

ANSWER: Because it is the production time that the allowance will be applied to on subsequent studies.

13. *What is meant by "occupational physiology"?*

ANSWER: That branch of study related to the worker and his environment.

14. *Define "attention time." Why is it necessary to apply an allowance to attention time?*

ANSWER: Time when the operator must observe the process to maintain the efficient progress of the operation.

To reward workers on jobs where a significant portion of the cycle is machine controlled, so that facilities will be kept running and operators of their facilities will be rewarded adequately for continuous operation of the equipment.

15. *Based upon the International Labor Office's tabulation, what would be the allowance factor on a work element involving a 42-pound pulling force if there was inadequate light and exacting work was required?*

ANSWER: Use of force (interpolating) = 9.8%
Bad light (inadequate) = 5.0%
Close attention (exacting) = 2.0%
Constant allowances = 9.0%
Total 25.8%

16. *Explain what relation, if any, there is between financial incentives and the effect of fatigue.*

ANSWER: Financial incentives will result in greater productivity of the employee. If heavy work is being done, the operator under financial incentive will be more tired than his counterpart under daywork (non-incentive) at the end of the working day.

17. *What are the advantages of having operators oil and clean their own machines?*

ANSWER: It gives them a change in their work pattern. It gives them a feel of responsibility for the equipment they operate and they usually perform these maintenance operations more conscientiously than others who may be assigned to this work.

18. *Why do many proponents of the MTM fundamental motion data system advocate that no allowance be provided for fatigue?*

ANSWER: Becaust MTM standard data values are based upon a work rate that readily can be sustained for the eight-hour working day by the average healthy employee.

GENERAL QUESTIONS

1. *Do you feel that the operation or the operator determines the extent to which personal delay time is utilized? Why or why not?*

ANSWER: This is a good question to discuss in detail. Both the operator and the operation affect the amount of personal delay time taken. Probably the greater portion of personal delay time taken is operator-related rather than operation-related.

2. *Why is fatigue allowance frequently applied only to the effort areas of the work cycle?*

ANSWER: Because in the non-effort portions of the cycle the operator can, in effect, be overcoming fatigue through sitting down (rest).

3. *Should fatigue allowances vary with the different shifts for a given class of work? Why or why not?*

ANSWER: Fatigue allowances should not vary with the different shifts unless there is a variation in method in the different shifts.

79

4. *What are the objections to determining fatigue allowances by measuring the decline of production not attributable to methods changes or personal or unavoidable delays?*

ANSWER: It is most difficult to measure the decline in production that is attributable to fatigue only. Sometimes (surprisingly so) there will be an increase in production near the end of the working day thus indicating negative fatigue exists, which is of course not possible.

5. *Give several reasons for not applying an "extra" allowance to operations when the major part of the cycle is machine controlled and the internal time is small compared to the cycle time.*

ANSWER: If the plant were on daywork (non-incentive) it would not be as important to include an extra allowance since under daywork the operators' hourly earnings would be compatible with others. Also it could be argued that in view of the large amount of machine controlled time, the operator alrady has adequate time to relax and requires no additional (extra) allowance time.

6. *With the extension of automation and the tendency of many companies to go to the four-day week, do you feel that personal allowances should be increased? Why or why not?*

ANSWER: This question warrants discussion. Certainly under the 10-hour working day more fatigue will result than in the 8-hour working day. However, the question addresses personal allowances. It would seem that the percentage personal allowance for the five-day week (8 hr./day) should be identical to the percentage personal allowance provided for the four-day week (10 hr./day).

7. *With reference to Figure 16–3, why did the time for assembly, after 85 blocks of work were completed, decrease?*

ANSWER: The time for the 80th through the 85th block of work increased—probably because of fatigue. The 86th to 90th block took less time than the 85th probably because the slowdown for the previous five blocks reduced the fatigue that had set in.

PROBLEMS

1. *The work measurement analyst is planning to develop a table of allowances for a given class of work in her maintenance department, using the work sampling technique. The areas for which she wants to establish allowances and the variation within which she expects to find the actual allowance 95 percent of the time are as follows:*

> *Personal allowance − 3 to 7 percent*
> *Crane wait − 2 to 6 percent*
> *Grind tools − 5 to 9 percent*
> *Avoidable delays − 1 to 4 percent*
> *Unavoidable delays − 10 to 20 percent*

How many random observations should she take? Over what period of time should she take these observations? Explain how she will determine when to take each day's observations?

ANSWER: The student is referred to Chapter 21 to work this problem.

The smallest anticipated delay will be for avoidable delays for which no allowance is added. However, we will use the expected value of this delay to compute the number of random observations since it will provide the largest number of observations.

$$n = \frac{\hat{P}(1 - \hat{P})}{\sigma_p{}^2} = \frac{.025(1 - .025)}{(.0075)^2} = 433 \text{ random observations}$$

These 433 random observations should be taken over at least a two-week (10 working day) period or 43 observations per working day. The exact time of day to take the 43 random observations can be based on a table of random numbers.

2. *Based on Table 16–3 develop an allowance factor for an assembly element where the operator is standing in a slightly awkward position, regularly lifts a weight of 15 pounds, has good light and atmospheric conditions. The attention required is fine, the noise level is continuous at 70 dBA, the mental strain is low, as is the monotony and the tediousness of the work.*

ANSWER:

Constant Allowance	–	9 percent
Standing	–	2 percent
Weight lifted (15 lbs.)	–	2 percent
Fine attention	–	2 percent
Total allowance		15 percent

17

_____

The standard time

TEXT QUESTIONS

1. *Define the term standard time.*

   ANSWER: It is the time required for an average operator, fully qualified and trained and working at a normal pace, to perform the operation.

2. *How is the conversion factor determined?*

   ANSWER: The conversion factor is found by multiplying the performance rating factor by one plus the applicable allowance.

3. *What would the conversion factor be in connection with Figure 17–1?*

   ANSWER: Conversion factor = performance rating factor × 1 + the applicable allowance. From Figure 17–1 conversion factor = 1.1 × 1.12 = 1.232.

4. *Why is it usually more convenient to express standards in terms of time per hundred pieces rather than time per piece?*

   ANSWER: Because the majority of industrial operations have short cycle times and ciphers can be avoided by expressing standard times in hours per hundred pieces. The hour is the basis of the wage rate and it is elementary to calculate earnings by multiplying the hourly rate of the operator by the standard in hours per hundred pieces by the number of hundreds produced.

5. *For what reason are temporary standards established?*

   ANSWER: On new operations where the operator has not had the opportunity to work long enough on the job to reach the flat portion of the learning curve.

6. *Express the standard of 5.761 minutes in terms of hours per hundred pieces. What would the operator's efficiency be if 92 pieces were completed during a working day? What would his efficiency be if he set up his machine (standard for setup = 0.45 hours) and produced 80 pieces during the eight-hour workday?*

   ANSWER: $\dfrac{5.761 \times 100}{60}$ = 9.602 hours/hundred

$$\frac{(0.92)(9.602)}{8} = 110.4 \text{ percent efficiency}$$

$$\frac{0.45 + (.80)(9.602)}{8} = 101.6 \text{ percent efficiency}$$

7. *What elements of work are included in the setup standard?*

   ANSWER: Punching in on job, getting tools from crib, getting drawings, setting up the machine or facility, punching out, removing tools from machine and returning them to the crib.

8. *What is the preferred method of handling setup time standards?*

   ANSWER: To establish setup standards as separate allowed times.

9. *How is the operator compensated on partial setups on hand screw machines?*

   ANSWER: When production runs are reasonably long, the operator often is given credit for the complete setup if the complete setup time is less than 1 hour.

10. *Determine the conversion factor and the allowed time for a job that had an average time of 5.24 minutes and carried a performance factor of 1.15 and an allowance of 12 percent.*

    ANSWER: $Ta = M_t C$
    $C = (1.15)(1.12) = 1.288$
    $M_t = 5.24$
    $Ta = (5.24)(1.288) = 6.749$ minutes allowed time.

11. *Explain why it is necessary that time standards be properly maintained.*

    ANSWER: So that they remain correct. Creeping method changes (that almost always take place) will obsolete a standards program that is not properly maintained.

12. *Explain how you would use learning curves in the establishment of temporary standards.*

    ANSWER: After measuring the time taken by the operator, performance rate the skill and effort demonstrated and apply the correct allowance. The learning curve would be used to establish an extra allowance applicable to a given number of parts to be produced. The extra allowance provided would be based on the slope of the applicable learning curve and the number of parts produced and number yet to be produced.

GENERAL QUESTIONS

1. *For what reasons might it be advantageous to express allowed times in minutes per piece?*

   ANSWER: For ease of understanding by the employee performing the work. For some workers the conversion of a standard in hours per hundred to minutes per piece or other unit of output may be difficult.

   If machine and/or operator money rates were based on the minute, then it would be desirable to express the work standard in minutes.

2. *How can the excessive use of temporary standards cause poor labor relations?*

   ANSWER: Since temporary standards are almost always looser than permanent standards, there is a desire by labor to make temporary standards permanent. Of course if this is done, then we have a poor standard as soon as the operator reaches the flat portion of the learning curve. If there are many temporary standards issued then there is more chance that some of them will not be restudied and converted to permanent standards.

3. *How does a company effectively maintain standards and avoid the reputation of being a "rate cutter"?*

    ANSWER: The best way to maintain a standards program is to audit all standards developed. The frequency of the audit is based upon the hours of application per standard per year. All permanent standards developed should be guaranteed as long as the method that was used when the standard was developed prevails.

4. *If an audit of a standard revealed that the standard as originally established was 20 percent loose, explain in detail the methodology to be followed to rectify the rate.*

    ANSWER: The instructor should spend some time discussing this question. The problem identified by this question is common in industry.

    If the quantity to be produced is quite large and the life of the job is long, an extensive methods study should be made; assuming method changes would be made, the job would be restudied and a new standard would be developed.

    If the life of the job is relatively short, then the company should live with the loose rate.

PROBLEMS

1. *Based upon the data provided in Figure 17–1, what would be the efficiency of an operator who set up the machine and produced an order of 5,000 pieces in a 40-hour work week?*

    ANSWER: $\dfrac{0.1129 \text{ (setup)} + (50 \times 0.8717)}{40} = 1.092$

    or an efficiency of 109%.

2. *Establish the money rate per hundred pieces from the following data:*

    Cycle time (average measured time): 1.23 minutes
    Base rate: $8.60 per hour
    Pieces per cycle: 4
    Machine time (power feed): 0.52 minutes per cycle
    Allowance: 17 percent on effort time; 12 percent on power feed time
    Element 1 average time: .09 minutes
    MTM time for element 1: 132 TMU. (one TMU = 0.00001 hr.)
    Plant uses synthetic performance rating

    ANSWER: Performance factor $= \dfrac{(60)(132)(0.00001)}{.09} = .88$

    Allowed machine time per piece $= \dfrac{(0.52)(1.00)(1.12)}{4} = 0.146$ min.

    Allowed effort time per piece $= \dfrac{(1.23 - .52)(.88)(1.17)}{4} = \underline{0.183}$ min.

    Allowed cycle time per piece $\qquad$ .329 min.

    Money rate per minute $= \dfrac{\$8.60}{60} = \$0.143$

    Money rate per hundred $= (\$0.143)(0.329)(100) = \$4.7047$

3. *The following data resulted from a time study taken on a horizontal milling machine:*

    Pieces produced per cycle: 8

    Average measured cycle time: 8.36 minutes

    Average measured effort time per cycle: 4.62 minutes

    Average rapid traverse time: 0.08 minutes

    Average cutting time power feed: 3.66 minutes

    Performance factor: + 15 percent

    Allowance (machine time): 10 percent

    Allowance (effort time): 15 percent

The operator works on the job a full eight-hour day and produces 380 pieces. How many standard hours does the operator earn? What is his efficiency for the eight-hour day?

ANSWER: Allowed power feed cycle time = $(3.66 + .08)(1.00)(1.10)$ = 4.114 min.

          Allowed effort time per cycle   = $(8.36 - 3.74)(1.15)(1.15)$ = <u>6.110 min.</u>

          Allowed cycle time =   10.224 min.

          Allowed piece time = $\dfrac{10.224}{8}$ = 1.278 min.

          $\dfrac{(1.278)(380)}{60}$ = 8.094 standard hours earned

          $\dfrac{8.094}{8}$ = 101.2% efficiency

18

Standard data

TEXT QUESTIONS

1. *What do we mean by "standard data"?*

   ANSWER: Standard data are elemental time standards that have been either taken from proven time studies, developed by stop watch measurement procedures, or developed through the use of fundamental motion data.

2. *What is the approximate ratio in the time required for setting standards by stopwatch methods and by standard data methods?*

   ANSWER: 5 to 1. For every standard established by the stopwatch procedure, about 5 can be established using the standard data procedure.

3. *What advantages are there to establishing time standards by using standard data rather than by taking individual studies?*

   ANSWER: They will be more consistent, standards can be established more rapidly, a less experienced person can be used to establish standards.

4. *What would the time mill slot depend upon?*

   ANSWER: The feed and speed of the milling cutter, the diameter of the cutter, the length of the cut, the applicable allowances.

5. *Of what use is the "fast" watch in the compilation of standard data?*

   ANSWER: The "fast" watch measures in terms of .001 minute. It is used to time individual elements in connection with standard data development. Since only one or two elements per cycle are measured the snapback procedure is used.

6. *Compute the times for elements a, b, c, d, and e when elements a + b + c were timed at 0.057 minute; b + c + d were found to equal 0.078 minute; c + d + e, 0.097 minute; d + e + a, 0.095 minute; and e + a + b, 0.069 minute.*

   ANSWER: By adding these five equations:

   $3a + 3b + 3c + 3d + 3e = 0.396$ min.
   $a + b + c + d + e = .396 \div 3 = 0.132$ min.
   $d + e = .132 - .057 = 0.075$ min.

   $a = .095 - 0.75 = 0.020$ min.
   $c = .097 - .075 = 0.022$ min.
   $b = .057 - .02 - .022 = 0.015$ min.
   $d = .078 - .015 - .022 = 0.041$ min.
   $e = .095 - .041 - .020 = 0.034$ min.

7. *What would be the lead of a 3/4 inch diameter drill with an included angle of 118°?*

ANSWER: $1 = \dfrac{r}{\tan A} = \dfrac{0.375}{\tan 59°} = 0.225$ inches

8. *What would be the feed in inches per minute of a 3/4 inch drill running at a surface speed of 80 feet per minute and a feed of 0.008 inch per revolution?*

ANSWER: $Fm = \dfrac{(3.82)(f)(Sf)}{d}$

$= \dfrac{(3.82)(0.008)(80)}{0.75}$

$= 3.26$ inches per minute

9. *How long would it take the above drill to drill through a casting 2 1/4 inches thick?*

ANSWER: $T = \dfrac{L}{Fm}$

$= \dfrac{2.25 + 0.225}{3.26}$

$= 0.76$ minutes

10. *How are feeds usually expressed in lathe work?*

ANSWER: Feeds are usually expressed in thousandths of an inch per revolution.

11. *How long would it take a turn 6 inches of 1-inch bar stock on a No. 3 W. and S. turret lathe running at 300 feet per minute and feeding at the rate of 0.005 inch per revolution?*

ANSWER: $T = \dfrac{L}{Fm}$

$Fm = \dfrac{(3.82)(S)(f)}{d} = \dfrac{(3.82)(300)(0.005)}{1} = 5.73$

$T = \dfrac{6}{5.73} = 1.047$ minutes

12. *A plain milling cutter 3 inches in diameter with a width of a face of 2 inches is being used to mill a piece of cold-rolled steel 1 1/2 inches wide and 4 inches long. The depth of cut is 3/16 inch. How long would it take to make the cut if the feed per tooth is 0.010 inch and a 16-tooth cutter running at a surface speed of 120 feet per minute is used?*

ANSWER: Lead of cutter $= \sqrt{1.5\ (1.5 - 0.1875)} = 0.433$ inches

$L = 4 + 0.433 = 4.433$ inches

$Fm = (f)(n)(N_r) = (.010)(16)(N_r)$

$N_r = \dfrac{3.82\ S_f}{d} = \dfrac{(3.82)(120)}{3} = 152.8$ rev/min.

$Fm = (.010)(16)(152.8) = 24.45$ inches per minute

$T = \dfrac{4.433}{24.45} = 0.18$ minutes cutting time.

13. *What are some of the disadvantages of using curves to tabulate standard data?*

   ANSWER: An error may be introduced because of interpolation or outright reading error. As they are used repeatedly they become marked making accurate reading difficult.

14. *What standard procedures should be followed in the plotting of simple curves?*

   ANSWER: Plot time on the ordinate and the independent variable on the abscissa. If practical, all scales should begin at zero. Select a scale for the independent variable to utilize fully the plotting paper.

15. *What would be the horsepower requirements of turning a mild steel shaft 3 inches in diameter if a cut of $1/4$ inch with a feed of 0.022 inches per revolution at a spindle speed of 250 rpm were established?*

   ANSWER: 250 rpm $= \dfrac{(250)(3)(\pi)}{12}$ surface feet/min.

   $= 196.34$ feet/min.

From the table A3–12:

   C $= 270,000$

   P $= $ CA

   $= (270,000)(0.022)(0.25)$

   $= 1,485$ chip pressure on tool in pounds

   H.P. $= \dfrac{(P)(S)}{33,000} = \dfrac{(1,485)(196.34)}{33,000} = 8.835$ horsepower

GENERAL QUESTIONS

1. *What do you think is the attitude of labor toward establishing standards through the use of standard data?*

   ANSWER: Have the students explore this question. Many unions do not favor the use of standard data because it prevents creeping looseness which often occurs in connection with stopwatch time study using performance rating.

2. *Using the drill press standard data shown in the text, preprice a drilling job with which you are familiar. How does this standard compare with the present rate on the job? (Be sure that identical methods are compared.)*

   REMARKS: If possible have the students perform this exercise. The two standards should be very similar.

3. *Does complete standard data supplant the stopwatch? Explain.*

   ANSWER: No, it does not. There will always be a certain amount of "do" elements performed by the process or manually that will need to be measured with the stopwatch.

4. *If you were president of your local union, would you advocate that standards be established by standard data? Why or why not?*

   ANSWER: This question is worthy of much discussion. Standards set with standard data will be more consistent so should cause fewer grievances. Also they should give a better data base for management, making the company more competitive. On the other hand, the union needs some problems to justify their existence to dues-paying members.

PROBLEMS

1. *The analyst in the Dorben Company made 10 independent time studies in the hand paint spraying section of the finishing department. The product line under study revealed a direct relation between spraying time and product surface area. The following data were collected:*

Study No.	Leveling Factor	Product Surface Area	Standard Time
1	0.95	170	0.32
2	1.00	12	0.11
3	1.05	150	0.31
4	0.80	41	0.14
5	1.20	130	0.27
6	1.00	50	0.18
7	0.85	120	0.24
8	0.90	70	0.23
9	1.00	105	0.25
10	1.10	95	0.22

Compute the slope and intercept constant, using regression line equations. How much spray time would you allow for a new part with a surface area of 250 square inches?

ANSWER:

Study No.	x or area	y or time	xy	x^2
1	170	0.32	54.4	28,900
2	12	0.11	1.32	144
3	150	0.31	46.5	22,500
4	41	0.14	5.74	1,681
5	130	0.27	35.1	16,900
6	50	0.18	9.0	2,500
7	120	0.24	28.8	14,400
8	70	0.23	16.1	4,900
9	105	0.25	26.25	11,025
10	95	0.22	20.9	9,025
	943	2.27	244.11	111,975

$$b = \frac{(\Sigma x^2)(\Sigma y) - (\Sigma x)(\Sigma xy)}{(N)(\Sigma x^2) - (\Sigma x)^2}$$

$$= \frac{(111,975)(2.27) - (943)(244.11)}{(10)(111,975) - (943)(943)}$$

$$= 0.104 \text{ minutes}$$

$$m = \frac{(N)(\Sigma xy) - (\Sigma x)(\Sigma y)}{(N)(\Sigma x^2) - (\Sigma x)^2}$$

$$= \frac{(10)(244.11) - (943)(2.27)}{(10)(111,975) - (943)(943)} = 0.0013$$

For 250 square inches: Time = $(0.0013)(250) + 0.104 = 0.429$ min.

2. *The work measurement analyst in the Dorben Company is desirous of developing an accurate equation for estimating the cutting of various configurations in sheet metal with a band saw. The data from eight time studies for the actual cutting element provided the following information:*

No.	Lineal inches	Standard time
1	10	0.40
2	42	0.80
3	13	0.54
4	35	0.71
5	20	0.55
6	32	0.66
7	22	0.60
8	27	0.61

What would be the relation between the length of cut and the standard time, using the least squares technique?

ANSWER:

Study	x or lineal inches	y or time	xy	x^2
1	10	0.40	4.0	100
2	42	0.80	33.6	1,764
3	13	0.54	7.02	169
4	35	0.71	24.85	1,225
5	20	0.55	11.0	400
6	32	0.66	21.12	1,024
7	22	0.60	13.2	484
8	27	0.61	16.47	729
	201	4.87	131.26	5,895

$\Sigma y = Nb + m \Sigma x$

$\Sigma xy = b \Sigma x + m \Sigma x^2$

$4.87 = 10b + 201m$

$131.26 = 201b + 5,895m$

$10b = 4.87 - 201m$

$201b = 131.26 - 5,895m$

$2,010b = 987.87 - 40,401m$

$\underline{2,010b = 1,312.60 - 58,950m}$

$\quad 0 = -333.73 + 18,549m$

$\quad m = 0.018$

$\quad b = 0.125$

91

3. *The work measurement analyst in the XYZ Company wishes to develop standard data involving fast, repetitive manual motions for use in a light assembly department. Because of the shortness of the desired standard data elements, he is obliged to measure them in groups as they are performed on the factory floor. On a certain study, he is endeavoring to develop standard data for five elements which will be denoted A, B, C, D, and E. Using a fast (0.001) decimal minute watch, the analyst studied a variety of assembly operations and arrived at the following data:*

$$A + B + C = 0.131 \text{ minutes}$$
$$B + C + D = 0.114 \text{ minutes}$$
$$C + D + E = 0.074 \text{ minutes}$$
$$D + E + A = 0.085 \text{ minutes}$$
$$E + A + B = 0.118 \text{ minutes}$$

Compute the standard data values for each of the elements A, B, C, D, and E.

ANSWER: $3A + 3B + 3C + 3D + 3E = 0.522$

$A + B + C + D + E = 0.522 \div 3 = 0.174$

$D + E = 0.174 - 0.131 = 0.043$ minutes

$A = 0.085 - 0.043 = 0.042$ minutes

$C = 0.074 - 0.043 = 0.031$ minutes

$B = 0.131 - 0.042 - 0.031 = 0.058$ minutes

$D = 0.114 - 0.058 - 0.031 = 0.025$ minutes

$E = 0.118 - 0.042 - 0.058 = 0.018$ minutes

4. *The work measurement analyst in the Dorben Company is developing standard data for prepricing work in the drill press department. Based upon the following recommended speeds and feeds, compute the power feed cutting time of $1/2$ inch high-speed drills with an 118° included angle to drill through material that is $1/8$ inch thick. Include a 10 percent allowance for P.D.&F.*

Material	Recommended speed (ft./min.)	Feed (in./rev.)
Al (copper alloy)	300	0.006
Cast iron	125	0.005
Monel (R)	50	0.004
Steel (1112)	150	0.005

ANSWER: Lead of drill $= \dfrac{r}{\tan A} = \dfrac{0.25}{\tan 59°} = 0.15$

Total length of hole $= 0.125 + 0.15 = 0.275$ in.

Al, feed in in./min. $= \dfrac{(3.82)(0.006)(300)}{0.50} = 13.750$

Cast iron, feed in in./min. $= \dfrac{(3.82)(0.005)(125)}{0.50} = 4.775$

Monel (R), feed in in./min. $= \dfrac{(3.82)(0.004)(50)}{0.50} = 1.528$

Steel (1112), feed in in./min. $= \dfrac{(3.82)(0.005)(150)}{0.50} = 5.73$

Cutting time allowed (Al) = $\left(\dfrac{0.275}{13.75}\right)$ (1.10) = 0.022 min.

Cutting time allowed (C.I.) = $\left(\dfrac{0.275}{4.775}\right)$ = (1.10) = 0.063 min.

Cutting time allowed (Monel–R) = $\left(\dfrac{0.275}{1.528}\right)$ (1.10) = 0.198 min.

Cutting time allowed (Steel–1112) = $\left(\dfrac{0.275}{5.73}\right)$ (1.10) = 0.053 min.

19

Basic motion times

TEXT QUESTIONS

1. *What are the advantages of using basic motion times?*

   ANSWER: The flexibility of basic motion times permits their use in any type of work. When properly applied by competent analysts, they establish consistent standards. They maintain a uniform concept of normal in connection with the basic motion time system used.

2. *What variables are considered by the Work-Factor technique?*

   ANSWER: The body member making the motion, the distance moved, the weight carried, and the manual control required (care, directional control or steering to a target, changing direction, stopping at a definite location).

3. *How did Work-Factor develop its values?*

   ANSWER: Work-Factor data were originally developed from four years of gathering data by the micromotion technique, stop-watch procedures, and the use of a specially constructed photo-electric time machine.

4. *What is the time value of one TMU?*

   ANSWER: 1 TMU equals 0.00001 hour.

5. *Who pioneered the MTM system?*

   ANSWER: Dr. Harold B. Maynard.

6. *What two other terms are used frequently to identify basic motion times?*

   ANSWER: Synthetic and predetermined times.

7. *Explain why most companies today require certification before they utilize basic motion times for the establishment of standards.*

   ANSWER: Because considerable specialized training is necessary before an individual is able to use these techniques consistently and accurately. Certification assures that this specialized training has been obtained.

8. *Would it be easy or difficult to perform a GB get with the left hand while performing a PC place with the right hand? Explain.*

ANSWER: It would be difficult. The student can confirm this by referring to Figure 19–9. A PC put (place) indicates there is more than one correcting motion required which would be difficult to perform simultaneously with any case of get except a simple contact grasp (A).

9. *Who was originally responsible for thinking in terms of developing standards for basic work divisions? What was his contribution?*

ANSWER: F. W. Taylor. The development of scientific management, the development of stop-watch time study, the development of the effect of various variables in the cutting of metal.

10. *Calculate the equivalent in TMUs of .0075 hours per piece; of 0.248 minutes per piece; of 0.0622 hours per hundred; of 0.421 seconds per piece; of 10 pieces per minute.*

ANSWER: 0.0075 hrs./pc. = 750 TMUs/pc.

0.248 min./pc. = 413 TMUs/pc.

0.0622 hrs./C = 6,220 TMUs/C

0.421 sec./pc. = 12 TMUs/pc.

10 pcs./min. = 10 pcs./1,667 TMUs

11. *How is MTM related to the analysis of method?*

ANSWER: To apply MTM, one must first make a detailed analysis of the method.

12. *For what reasons was MTM–2 developed? Where does MTM–2 have special application?*

ANSWER: To further the application of MTM to work areas where the detail of MTM–1 would economically preclude its use.

It has application where the effort portion of the work cycle is more than one minute, the cycle is not highly repetitive, the manual portion of the work cycle does not involve a large number of either complex or simultaneous hand motions.

13. *What classes of action are recognized by MTM–2?*

ANSWER: Five distance classes: 0–2 inches, 2–6 inches, 6–12 inches, 12–18 inches, and over 18 inches. Also the categories of: GET, PUT, GET WEIGHT, PUT WEIGHT, REGRASP, APPLY PRESSURE, EYE ACTION, FOOT ACTION, STEP, BEND AND ARISE, CRANK.

14. *Explain the relationship of basic motion times to standard data.*

ANSWER: Basic motion times, in reality, are refined standard data. These basic times can be used to develop standard data elements so that standards may be developed rapidly.

15. *If you have finished drilling a hole 3 inches deep on a Western radial drill, how long would it take to present the drill and drill a second hole in a steel forging ¹/₂ inch in diameter and 3 inches deep? Traverse 6 inches; swing of head: 8 inches: 0.007 inch feed; 50 feet per minute surface speed.*

ANSWER: Handling: From Table 19–10 (up spindle, swing and traverse head, and down spindle) = .084.

Drill hole: Drill $3 + \dfrac{.25}{1.6643} = 3.15$ inches.

Fm = (3.82)(.007)(50) = 1.337 in./min.

Drill time $= \dfrac{3.15}{1.337} = \underline{2.356 \text{ min.}}$

2.440 min.

96

16. *How has Work-Factor endeavored to take care of the additivity of the elements of a motion pattern?*

ANSWER: None of the basic motion time systems including Work-Factor have entirely taken care of the additivity of the elements of a motion pattern. By providing Work-Factors as an index of additional time required over and above the basic time for identifying the effect of the variables of manual control, some consideration is given subsequent motions because of the identity of a specific motion taking place.

GENERAL QUESTIONS

1. *What does the future hold for synthetic basic time values?*

ANSWER: It should be brought out that one of the major objections to establishing standards with basic motion data is the time it takes to identify and evaluate all the motion patterns involved in performing an operation. With the capabilities of data processing equipment, these clerical steps can be performed much more rapidly and accurately. The future for the application of basic time values is excellent.

2. *Which of the two techniques outlined is easier to apply?*

REMARKS: Have the students establish a standard on a simple job such as assembling a cable clamp using both MTM and Work-Factor. Then have them discuss the positive and negative points of each system.

3. *Which method, in your opinion, will give the most reliable results? Why?*

REMARKS: Now have the students establish a standard on the job mentioned in question two above using stop-watch procedure. Compare all three results.

4. *Describe as vividly as you can how you would explain to a worker in your forge shop who knows nothing about MTM what it is and how it is applied.*

REMARKS: The point to bring out is that MTM is applied only after a careful study of the method being employed. All movements in the worker's motion pattern are considered in the establishment of the standard.

5. *Give several objections to the application of MTM which you might receive from a worker, and explain how you would overcome them.*

REMARKS: Workers may ask how they can be sure that no motion patterns were omitted. The response should be that the left and right hand breakdown establishes as a record all the motion patterns performed by the operator.

Workers may ask why the stop-watch is not used for the entire study, since the time for the "use" or "do" is determined by stop-watch procedure. The response might be that management wants to use the fairest and best measurement tools available. Since basic motion times are not performance rated they are preferable.

6. *Some companies have been experiencing a tendency for their time study people to become more liberal in their performance rating over a period of years. How do fundamental motion data offset this tendency toward creeping loose standards?*

ANSWER: Since it is not necessary to performance rate fundamental motion data, it is not possible for creeping loose standards, except through more generous allowances, with the passing of time.

7. *Is there consistency between MTM–1 and MTM–2 in the handling of simultaneous motions?*

REMARKS: Have students study in detail Table 19–4(X) and Figure 19–9 and note the consistencies in the handling of simultaneous motions.

8. *If MTM–3 were used to study an operation of approximately three minutes, what could you say about the accuracy of the standard?*

   ANSWER: Three minutes equal 5,000 TMU. By referring to Figure 19–12 and recording the intersection of 5,000 TMU with the MTM–3 curve, a total absolute accuracy at 90% confidence level of 7.5% is obtained.

PROBLEMS

1. *Determine the time for the dynamic component of M20B20.*

   ANSWER: M20B20 = 18.2 + static component (7.4) + dynamic component (.22 × 18.2).

   Dynamic component = 0.22 × 18.2 = 4 TMU.

2. *A 30-pound bucket of sand having a coefficient of 0.40 is pushed 15 inches away from the operator with both hands. What would be the normal time for the move?*

   ANSWER: Because both hands are used, it is assumed that resistance is evenly balanced between both hands. Total resistance equals 30 × .40 = 12 lb.

   M15B12 = 14.6 + (.5)(1.2) + 3.9 + (.11)(14.6 + .5 × 1.2) = 15.2 + 3.9 + 1.672 = 20.77 TMU.

3. *A ³/₄ inch diameter coin is placed within a 1 inch diameter circle. What would be the normal time for the position element?*

   ANSWER: Tolerance is ¹/₈"; therefore the position (based on MTM) is PISE or 5.6 TMUs.

4. *Give the MTM breakdown required to grasp the cotter pin with the pliers shown in the following sketch.*

   ANSWER: We will make the assumption that the right hand holding the pliers moves 6" prior to grasping the cotter pin.

Move right hand 6 inches to approximate location	M6B –	10.2 TMU
Spread pliers with little finger	M1B –	2.9 TMU
Regrasp	G2 –	5.6 TMU
Position pliers	PISE –	5.6 TMU
Close pliers	AP–1 –	16.2 TMU
Total:		40.6 TMUs

20

Formula construction

TEXT QUESTIONS

1. *How can MTM and Work-Factor be used in formula development?*

   ANSWER: These fundamental motion data techniques can be used to develop elemental time standards that can serve as input data for formula development.

2. *What advantages does the formula offer over standard data in establishing time standards?*

   ANSWER: Standards established by formula are more rapidly developed; they can be established by a less experienced analyst; there is less chance of an error.

3. *Is the use of time study formulas restricted to machine shop operations where feeds and speeds influence allowed times? Explain.*

   ANSWER: No, time formulas are applicable to practically all types of work. They have been successfully used in office operations, foundry work, maintenance work, painting, machine work, forging, etc.

4. *What are the characteristics of a sound time study formula?*

   ANSWER: It must be reliable. It should be as clear, concise, and simple as possible.

5. *What is the danger of using too few studies in the derivation of a formula?*

   ANSWER: Insufficient data points can lead to significant inaccuracies in the plotting of curves and the resulting algebraic expressions.

6. *What is the function of the synthesis in the fomula report?*

   ANSWER: To give a complete explanation of the derivation of the various components entering into the formula so as to facilitate its use.

7. *Write the equation of the ellipse with its center at the origin and axes along the coordinate axes and passing through (2, 3) and (−1, 4).*

   ANSWER: $Ax^2 + By^2 = C$ or $\dfrac{x^2}{b^2} + \dfrac{y^2}{a^2} = 1$

   solving with data points: $7x^2 + 3y^2 = 55$

8. *Find the equation of the hyperbola with its center at (0,0) and a = 4, b = 5 foci on the y axis.*

ANSWER: $a^2 x^2 - b^2 y^2 = -a^2 b^2$ or $\dfrac{x^2}{b^2} - \dfrac{y^2}{a^2} = 1$

$$\dfrac{x^2}{25} - \dfrac{y^2}{16} = 1$$

9. *What 14 sections make up the formula report?*

ANSWER: Formula number, part, operation, work station, normal time, application, analysis, procedure, time studies, table of detail elements, synthesis, inspection, wage payment, signature of constructor and approver.

10. *What nine steps represent the chronological procedure in the design of time study formulas?*

ANSWER: Determine what class of work is involved; determine what range of work is to be measured; collect formula data; analyze constants and variables; develop synthesis; check formula data for accuracy, consistency, and ease of application; write formula report; install formula; follow up the installation to be sure results are satisfactory.

11. *Explain in detail how it is possible to solve graphically for time when two variables are influential and they cannot be combined.*

ANSWER: Construct a graphic relationship with time for each variable. One chart will plot the relationship between time and one of the variables in selected studies in which the values of the other variables tend to remain constant. The second chart will show the relationship between the second variable and time, adjusted to remove the influence of the first variable.

12. *Develop an algebraic expression for the relationship between time and area from the following data:*

Study No.	1	2	3	4	5
Time	4	7	11	15	21
Area	28.6	79.4	182	318	589

ANSWER:

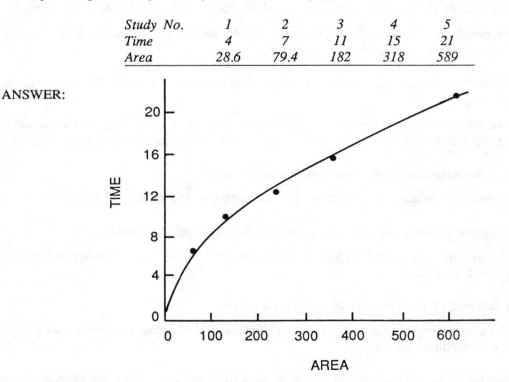

$Y^2 = 2px$ (equation of parabola with origin at the vertex and the x-axis the axis of the parabola).

Solving five equations for p we get p = 0.33

Time = $\sqrt{0.66\ \text{Area}}$

13. *If the data show in Figure 20–1 were plotted on logarithmic paper, would the plotting be a straight line? Why or why not?*

ANSWER: The data associated with the elements "fill partly full of sand," "ran," and "fill and ran" would not plot as straight line because two variables (volume, and length/diameter) affect time.

14. *What types of problems lend themselves to solution on the digital computer?*

ANSWER: Line balancing, labor efficiency reporting, applying time study formulas, analyzing time study data, and developing new standards based on fundamental motion data, formulas, and work sampling data.

GENERAL QUESTIONS

1. *Would the company union prefer standards to be set by formulas or standard data? Why or Why not?*

ANSWER: Have the students discuss this question. Usually the union will prefer stop-watch time study for establishing standards. They do not like either standard data or formula because these techniques will never allow "creeping looseness."

2. *Would it be necessary for the "chart and formula" designator to have a background in time study work? Why or Why not?*

ANSWER: Not really necessary but it would be helpful. Especially in deciding what data should be considered a constant and what a variable. With a background in time study, the chart and formula worker will also understand better the variables that influence time.

3. *If an operator objected strongly to a rate established through a formula, explain in detail how you would endeavor to prove to him that the rate was fair.*

ANSWER: The best way is to conduct a detailed stop-watch time study.

PROBLEMS

1. *In the Dorben Company, the work measurement analyst planned to develop standard data on a new milling machine that was recently installed. The material being cut in one group of studies involved a 1 1/4 inch width of cut, with lengths varying from 4 inches to 30 inches. For this work a plain carbide-tipped milling cutter 3 inches in diameter and a width of face of 2 inches was being used. Depths of cut ranged from $^3/_{16}$ inch to $^7/_{16}$ inch.*

Give the equation that can be programmed to provide cutting time in terms of d (depth of cut) and l (length of casting being milled). In all cases, the feed per tooth is 0.010 inch and the 16-tooth cutter is running at a surface speed of 80 feet per minute.

ANSWER: Time $= \dfrac{\text{Length of Casting} + \text{Lead of Cutter}}{\text{Feed}}$

$$= \frac{1 + 2.25 - (1.5-d)}{(16)(0.010)\ [(3.82)(80) \div 3]}$$

$$= \frac{1 + 2.25 - (1.5-d)}{16.3}$$

Where l varies from 4 to 30 inches and d from $^3/_{16}$ to $^7/_{16}$ inch.

101

2. The work measurement analyst in the Dorben Company was studying the hand filing and polishing of external radii. Six studies provided the following information:

Study	Size of radii	Minutes per inch
1	3/8	0.24
2	1/2	0.37
3	5/8	0.59
4	11/16	0.80
5	3/4	0.93
6	1	1.52

These data plotted as a straight line on semilog paper where time (the dependent variable) was the logarithetic scale. Develop an algebraic equation for estimating the time of filing and polishing various radii.

ANSWER: Select two points:

$x = 1 \qquad y = \log 1.52$

$x = \frac{3}{8} \qquad y = \log 0.24$

$m = \dfrac{\log 1.52 - \log 0.24}{1 - \frac{3}{8}} = 1.2826$

To determine equation:

$\log y - \log 1.52 = 1.28\,(x - 1)$

$\log y = 1.28x - 1.10$

$y = AB^x$

$\log y = \log A + x \log B$

$\log A = -1.10$

$A = 0.07944$

$\log B = 1.28$

$B = 19.05$

Filing time $= (0.08)(19.05)^r$

where r = radius being filed.

3. In the assembly department of the Dorben Company, various hardware is bagged for shipment. The time study analyst desires to design a formula or a system of curves to establish standards on this work. From the master table of detailed time studies, the following information was gathered for the second element, which was "place hardware components in bag."

Study No.	Time (min.)	Weight of Components (16)	Bag Size	No. of Component
1	0.264	6.61	4	11
2	0.130	1.15	2	6
3	0.186	5.61	3	8
4	0.169	2.91	2	6
5	0.126	4.01	2	4
6	0.220	6.14	3	9
7	0.200	5.50	3	6
8	0.332	7.02	4	14
9	0.222	7.02	4	6
10	0.155	1.75	2	8
11	0.345	5.45	4	17
12	0.256	6.91	4	10

From these data design a formula or a system of curves for establishing the standard for this element.

ANSWER: Consider the two variables "no. of components" and "weight of components" as of major influence on time. Plot weight of components against time for bags containing six components.

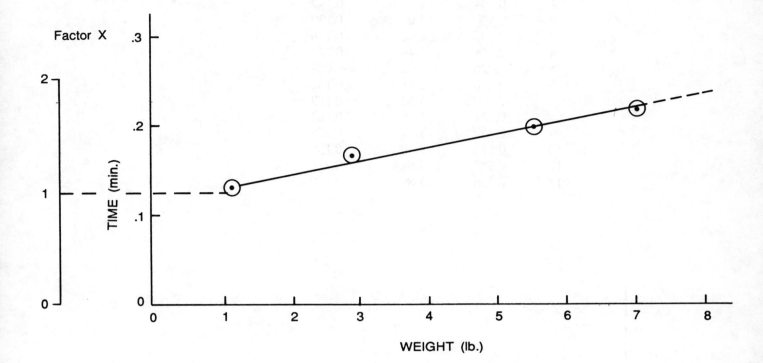

Now plot corrected time against number of components where corrected time equals stop-watch time/factor x value.

Study No.	Time (min.)	Factor X	Corrected time
1	0.264	1.8	0.147
2	0.130	1.0	0.130
3	0.186	1.6	0.116
4	0.169	1.4	0.121
5	0.126	1.42	0.089
6	0.220	1.65	0.133
7	0.200	1.58	0.127
8	0.332	1.80	0.184
9	0.222	1.77	0.125
10	0.155	1.18	0.131
11	0.345	1.6	0.216
12	0.256	1.8	0.142

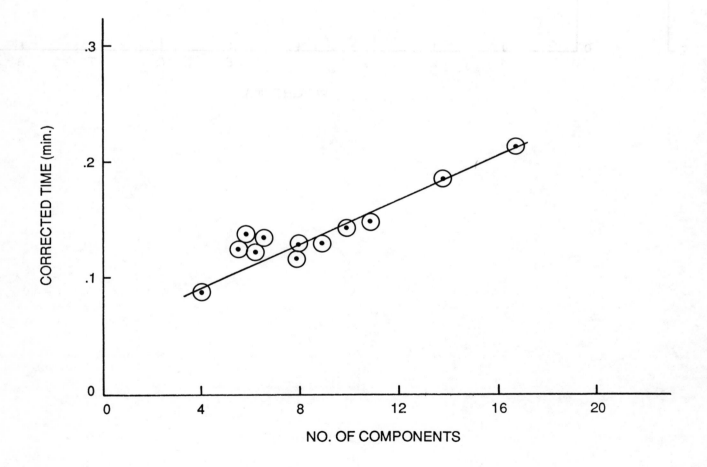

4. *In the blanking of various leather components from animal skins, the analyst noted a relationship between standard time and the area of the component. After taking five independent time studies, he observed the following:*

Study No.	Area of leather component (sq. in.)	Standard Time (min.)
1	5.0	0.07
2	7.5	0.10
3	15.5	0.13
4	25.0	0.20
5	34.0	0.24

Derive an algebraic expression to preprice the blanking of the various leather components.

ANSWER:

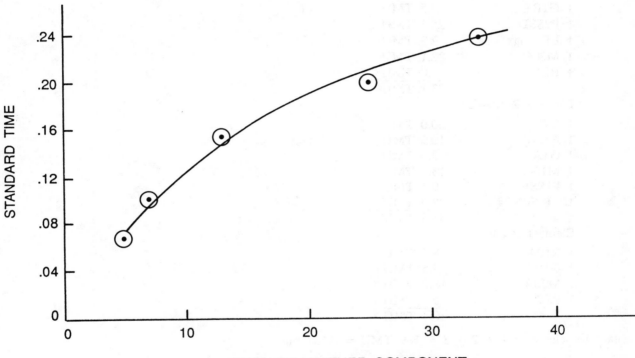

Data appears to be of the form $y^2 = 2\,px$ (parabola). From data mean value of p is computed and expression is:

Time = $\sqrt{0.0014 \text{ area of leather component}}$

5. *The analyst in the Dorben Company decides to develop a formula for prepricing a particular assembly operation involving different sizes of work. The asssembly operation involves three constant elements and one variable element. The constant elements are determined from MTM data. The classifications of the fundamental motions on the constant elements are as follows:*

Element 1: One R10C, one G1B, one P2SSD, one EF (max) one M20C with 2# weight, and one RL (case 1).

Element 2: One eye travel with T = 20 and D = 10, one R12B, one G1A, one M10C, one PISSE, ten T 30° 2#.

Element 3: One R10A, one G1B, one M20B, one RL2.

The variable element is based on the following data:

Study No.	Standard time (min.)	Surface area (sq.in.)
1	0.282	7.0
2	0.163	5.0
3	0.022	2.0
4	0.120	4.5
5	0.227	6.0

Develop the algebraic expression for establishing standards for this operation for parts with surface areas of up to seven square inches.

ANSWER: Element 1 equals:

1 R10C	12.9TMU
1 G1B	3.5 TMU
1 P2SSD	25.3 TMU
1 EF (max)	7.3 TMU
1 M20C	22.1 TMU
1 RL1	2.0 TMU
	73.1 TMU

Element 2 equals:

1 ETT	20.0 TMU
1 R12B	12.9 TMU
1 G1A	2.0 TMU
1 M10C	13.5 TMU
1 P1SSE	9.1 TMU
10 T 30° 2#	28.0 TMU
	85.5 TMU

Element 3 equals:

1 R10A	8.7 TMU
1 G1B	3.5 TMU
1 M20B	18.2 TMU
1 RL2	0 TMU
	30.4 TMU

Constant for elements 1 + 2 + 3 = 189 TMU = .1134 min.

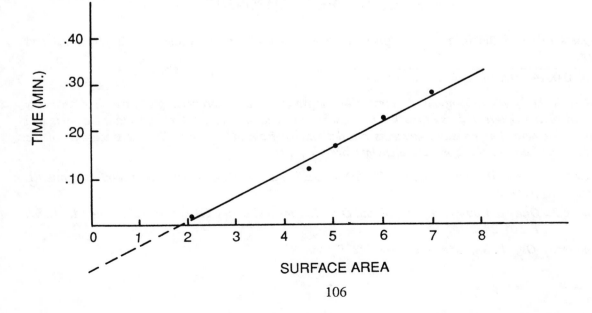

Linear relationship.

$$m = \frac{.282 - .022}{7 - 2} = 0.052$$

$b = -0.08$

Standard time $= (0.052)(\text{area}) + 0.0334$

6. *The industrial engineer in the Dorben Company is in the process of building a formula to preprice the manufacture of a line of specialty forgings. The data gathered indicated a nonlinear relationship between forging volume and standard time for the variable elements related to positioning in the die and the actual forging. The data taken were as follows:*

Study No.	Time (min.)	Forging Volume (cu. in.)
1	0.130	30
2	0.110	24
3	0.103	20
4	0.088	10
5	0.083	5
6	0.120	27

Develop an algebraic expression for the computation of standard time for any forging having a volume of between 5 and 30 cubic inches.

ANSWER:

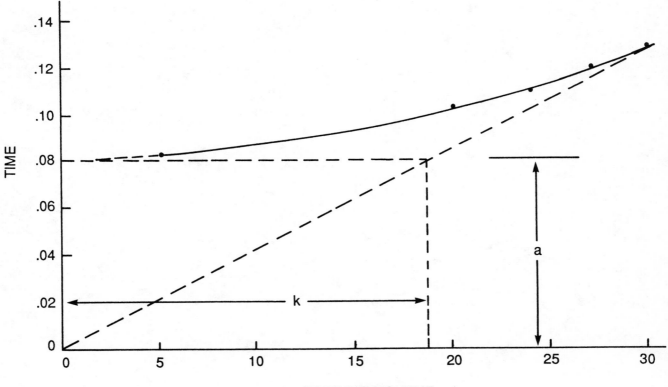

Plotting takes the form of a segment of a hyperbola:

$$\text{Time} = \sqrt{a^2 + \frac{(v^2)(a^2)}{k^2}}$$
$$= \sqrt{0.0064 + v^2\ 0.000018}$$

Example: $V = 10$

$T = \sqrt{0.0064 + (10^2)}$
$\quad = 0.091$ min.

21

Work sampling studies

TEXT QUESTIONS

1. *Where was work sampling first used?*

   ANSWER: In the British textile industry.

2. *What advantages are claimed for the work sampling procedure?*

   ANSWER: It does not require continuous observation, clerical time is diminished, fewer analyst work-hours expended, the operator is not subjected to long-period stop-watch observations, crew operations regularly studied by a single analyst.

3. *In what areas does work sampling have application?*

   ANSWER: Determining facility and personnel activity, establishing indirect and direct labor standards, determining allowances, determining machine utilization.

4. *How many observations should be recorded in determining the allowance for personal delays in a forge shop if it is expected that a 5 percent personal allowance will suffice, and if this value is to remain between 4 and 6 percent 95 percent of the time?*

   ANSWER: $n = \dfrac{\hat{p}(1 - \hat{p})}{\sigma\hat{p}^2} = \dfrac{.05(1 - .05)}{(.005)^2} = 1{,}900$ observations

5. *How is it possible to determine the time of day to make the varous observations so that biased results will not occur?*

   ANSWER: Use a table of random numbers or a random number generator and convert the random numbers into specific times of the day. For example, in a 100 number random table the value of one number would be 480 working minutes per day divided by 100, or 4.8 minutes.

6. *What considerations should be kept in mind when taking work sampling studies?*

   ANSWER: Explain and sell the work sampling method before using it, confine individual studies to similar groups of machines or operations, use as large a sample size as is practicable, take individual observations at random times so that observations will be recorded for all hours of the day, and take the observations over a reasonably long period.

7. *What is meant by stratifying the data collected? Explain when it would be desirable to stratify data.*

ANSWER: Stratifying data collected implies a certain amount of data will be collected over an established interval and there will be a predetermined number of intervals over which data is collected so that the total pool of data collected will approximate reality.

It is usually desirable to stratify data collected when making work sampling studies so that the study period is adequate to typify normal conditions. Many analysts feel that there should be at least two weeks of data collection.

8. *What are the principal advantages of using a random reminder in connection with the gathering of data for a work sampling study?*

ANSWER: The random reminder saves the time required to predetermine (by random number table, etc.) the times during the day that the analyst should go to the work area under study to gather data. More important, this instrument permits the analyst to concentrate on other work during the day when he/she is not gathering work sampling data. If the analyst bases his/her trips to the work area on a predetermined schedule, attention is addressed continually to the time of day in connection with the next scheduled trip making it difficult to concentrate on other work.

9. *To get ± 5 percent precision on work that is estimated to take 80 percent of the worker's time, how many random observations will be required at the 95 percent confidence level?*

ANSWER: $n = \dfrac{\hat{p}(1 - \hat{p})}{\sigma_{\hat{p}}^2}$

$4\sigma = (0.10)(.8) = 0.08$

$\sigma = 0.02$

$n = \dfrac{(.80)(1 - 0.8)}{(0.02)2}$

$= 400$ random observations

10. *If the average handling activity during a 10-day study is 82 percent, and the number of daily observations is 48, how much tolerance can be allowed on each day's percentage activity?*

ANSWER: $n = \dfrac{\hat{p}(1 - \hat{p})}{\sigma_{\hat{p}}^2}$

$(10)(48) = \dfrac{.82(1 - .82)}{\sigma_{\hat{p}}^2}$

$\sigma = 0.0175$

At 95% confidence level $(\pm\ 2\ \sigma) = \pm\ 0.035$.

11. *If it should develop that four seconds of time would be desirable for each random observation, and if a sample size of 2,000 is necessary, how often would the analyst need to service the random activity analysis camera?*

ANSWER: 4 seconds × 2,000 = 8,000 seconds of observation. Assume 1 frame per second or 8,000 frames would be consumed. With 16 mm. film, we have 40 frames per foot.

100 feet × 40 = 4,000 frames/100 foot roll.

$\dfrac{8,000 \text{ frames}}{4,000 \text{ frames}} = 2$ rolls of film.

Thus camera would need to be reloaded once after original loading.

12. *Over how long a period is it desirable to continue to acquire sampling data?*

ANSWER: Until a cumulative plot of the information being sought levels off.

13. *How biased can we expect work sampling data to be? Will this bias vary with the work situation? Explain.*

ANSWER: Based upon the study provided in the text, work sampling is about 12 percent biased. This bias will vary with the work situation. If, for example, data is used only after the first several days of a work sampling study, then that data is less likely to be biased.

GENERAL QUESTIONS

1. *Is there an application for work sampling in determining fatigue? Explain.*

ANSWER: Yes, work sampling can be used to determine the amount of fatigue. Observations made late in the day will indicate the operator is working less and using more time for rest, avoidable delays, and the like. Much of this decline in productivity during the period near the end of the day is attributable to fatigue.

2. *How can the validity of work sampling be sold to the employee not familiar with probability and statistical procedure?*

ANSWER: By making a number of throws of a coin and a pair of dice, and plotting the results. In this way the idea of number of observations required to get a good prediction of a known event can be achieved.

3. *What are the pros and cons for using work sampling to establish standards of performance?*

ANSWER: Pros: Eliminates the use of a stop-watch, is quite efficient, allows several standards to be established simultaneously, establishes standards on work that is difficult to measure.

Cons: Standards are likely to be loose because of bias in the acquired data. It is difficult to establish a reliable performance rating factor. Since data is collected over a relatively long period (two weeks or more) standards cannot be established quickly.

PROBLEMS

1. *The analyst in the Dorben Reference Library decides to use the work sampling technique to establish standards. Twenty employees are involved. The operations include cataloging, charging books out, returning books to their proper location, cleaning books, record keeping, packing books for shipment, and handling correspondence.*

A preliminary investigation resulted in the estimate that 30 percent of the time of the group was spent in cataloging. How many work sampling observations would be made if it were desirable to be 95 percent confident that the observed data were within a tolerance of plus or minus 10 percent of the population data? Describe how the random observations should be made.

The following table illustrates some of the data gathered from 6 of the 20 employees. From this data determine a standard in hours per hundred for cataloging.

Item		Operators				
	Smith	Apple	Brown	Green	Baird	Thomas
Total hours worked	78	80	80	65	72	75
Total observations (all elements)	152	170	181	114	143	158
Observations involving cataloging	50	55	48	29	40	45
Average rating	90	95	105	85	90	100

The number of volumes cataloged equals 14,612.

Design a control chart based on three-sigma limits for the daily observations.

ANSWER:
$$n = \frac{\hat{p}(1 - \hat{p})}{\sigma_p^2}$$

$$= \frac{0.30\ (1 - 0.30)}{(.015)^2}$$

$$= 933 \text{ random observations}$$

The random observations should be taken over at least a two-week period (10 working days). Thus about 93 random observations should be taken each day for a 10-day period. The exact time of day that the observations will be taken can be developed from a table of random numbers.

$$T_n = \frac{(n)(T)(P)}{(Pa)(N)} \text{ where:}$$

n = total observations of element under study
= 50 + 55 + 48 + 29 + 40 + 45
= 267

T = total operator time represented by study
= 78 + 80 + 80 + 65 + 72 + 75
= 450 hours

P = performance rating factor
$$= \frac{.90 + .95 + 1.05 + .85 + .90 + 1.00}{6}$$
= .94

Pa = total production for period
= 14,612 volumes cataloged

N = total observations of study
= 152 + 170 + 181 + 114 + 143 + 138
= 918

Tn = 0.0084198 hrs./volume
= 0.842 hrs./c + allowances

For control chart:

$$p = 0.30$$

$$100 = \text{sample size taken each day}$$

$$\sigma = \sqrt{\frac{\hat{p}(1-\hat{p})}{n}}$$

$$= \sqrt{\frac{.30(1-.30)}{100}}$$

$$= 0.0458$$

$$3\sigma = 0.1374 \text{ control limits}$$

Upper control limit = $0.30 + .14 = .44$
Lower control limit = $0.30 - .14 = .16$

2. *The work measurement analyst in the Dorben Company is planning to establish standards on indirect labor by using the work sampling technique. This study will provide the following information:*

    T = Total operator time represented by the study.
    N = Total number of observartions involved in the study.
    n = Total observations of the element under study.
    P = Production for the period under study.
    R = Average performance rating factor during the study.

With the above information derive the equation for estimating the normal elemental time for an operation (tn).

ANSWER: $T \times R$ = normal hours spent during the study.

$n \div N$ = percentage of total time spent on a given operation.

$(n \div N)(T)(R)$ = total normal hours spent on a given operation.

$\dfrac{(n \div N)(T)(R)}{P}$ = normal hours for one unit of output of a given operation = tn.

$\dfrac{(n \div N)(T)(R)}{P}$ + allowances = standard time for performing a given operation.

3. *The analyst in the Dorben Company wishes to measure the percentage of downtime in the drop hammer section of the forge shop. The superintendent estimated the downtime to be about 30 percent. The desired results, using a work sampling study, are to be within plus or minus 5 percent of "p" with a level of significance of 0.95.*

The analyst decides to take 300 random readings a day for a period of three weeks. Develop a "p" chart for "p" = 0.30 and subsample size N = 300. Explain the use of this "p" chart.

ANSWER:
$$3\sigma_p = 3\sqrt{\frac{p(1-p)}{n}}$$

$$= 3\sqrt{\frac{0.30(1-0.30)}{300}}$$

$$= .07937$$

Set up three sigma limits of ± 0.08 and p = .30.

Each day take readings and plot p. If daily readings are within the ± 0.08 tolerance, then we can continue with daily sample size of 300 until three weeks of observations have been taken and then compute the final estimated value of p from the data.

4. *The Dorben Company is using the work sampling technique to establish standards in its typing pool section. This pool has varied responsibilities, including typing from tape recordings, filing, Kardex posting, and duplicating. The pool has six typists who work a 40-hour week. Seventeen hundred random observations were made over a four-week period. During the period, 1,852 pages of routine typing were produced. Of the random observations, 1,225 showed that typing was taking place. Assuming a 20 percent P.D.&F. allowance and an adjusted performance rating factor of 0.85, calculate the hourly standard per page of typing.*

ANSWER: $Tn = \dfrac{(n)(T)(P)}{(Pa)(N)}$

and $Ta = Tn + \text{Allowances}$

$= (1.20)(Tn)$

$Tn = \dfrac{(1,225)(960)(0.85)}{(1,852)(1,700)} = 0.31749 \text{ hrs/page}$

$Ta = (1.20)(0.318)$

$= 0.3816 \text{ hrs. per page.}$

22

Establishing standards on indirect and expense work

TEXT QUESTIONS

1. *What would be the expected waiting time per shipment if it were established through stop-watch time study that the normal time to prepare a shipment was 15.6 minutes? Twenty-one shipments are made every shift (eight hours) The standard deviation of the service time has been estimated as 1.75 minutes. It is assumed that the arrivals are Poisson distributed and that the servicing time is arbitrary.*

ANSWER: $w = \left[\dfrac{uh}{2(1-u)}\right]\left[1 + \left(\dfrac{\sigma}{h}\right)^2\right]$

u = servers' occupancy ratio

$\quad = \dfrac{ah}{s}$

$\quad = \left[\dfrac{(21/8)(15.6/60)}{1}\right]$

$\quad = \dfrac{(2.625)(0.26)}{1}$

$\quad = 0.6825$

$w = \left[\dfrac{(0.6825)(15.6/60)}{2(1-0.6825)}\right]\left[1 + \left(\dfrac{1.75/15.6}{60}\right)^2\right]$

$\quad = \left[\dfrac{0.17745}{0.635}\right]\left[1 + 45.30\right]$

$\quad = 12.94$ minutes expected waiting time

2. *Using Monte Carlo methods, what would be the expected downtime hours because of the lack of an operator for servicing if four operators were assigned to the work situation described in the text?*

ANSWER: Refer to the simulation shown on pages 582 thru 588. Analyze as follows for hours 6 and 7.

```
                6 hour                          7 hour
Op. 1  |      6.1 = 1 hr.           |          7.1 = 1  hr.        |

Op. 2  |    6.2 = 0.9 hr.    |  6.5 = .2  |    7.2 = .8 hr.   |

Op. 3  |    6.3 = 0.9 hr.    |           |        7.3 = .9 hr.    |

Op. 4  |     6.4 = 1 hr.     |
```

Therefore due to 5th breakdown, this machine must wait 0.9 hours to be serviced during the 6th hour. No lost time for need of an operator during the 7th hour. Proceed as above for the entire 80-hour simulation.

3. *Differentiate between indirect labor and expense labor.*

ANSWER: Indirect labor is usually associated with those indirect factory workers such as: shipping and receiving, trucking, stores, inspection, material handling, toolroom, janitorial, and maintenance. Expense personnel include those indirect positions not coming under direct or indirect labor such as: office clerical, accounting, sales, engineering, etc.

4. *Explain what is meant by "queuing theory."*

ANSWER: Queuing theory is the mathematical analysis of the laws governing arrivals, service times, and the order in which arriving units are taken into service.

5. *What four divisions constitute indirect and expense work?*

ANSWER: Direct work, transportation, indirect work, and unnecessary work.

6. *How are standards established on the "unnecessary and delays" portion of indirect and expense work?*

ANSWER: Unnecessary indirect work and delays are removed from the work cycle through methods engineering. For those delays that cannot be removed an allowance is provided which is added to the normal time.

7. *The arrivals at the company cafeteria are Poisson, with an average time between arrivals of 1.75 minutes during the lunch period. The average time for a customer to obtain his lunch is 2.81 minutes, and this service time is distributed exponentially. What is the probability that a person arriving at the cafeteria will have to wait, and how long can he expect to wait?*

ANSWER: $u = \dfrac{ah}{s}$

$$= \dfrac{(0.57)(2.81)}{1}$$

$P > 0 = u = 1.60$ servers' occupancy ratio.

With but one server, it will be certain that an arrival will need to wait. If two servers are employed there will be a 0.80 probability that an arrival will have to wait.

8. *Why has there been a marked increase in the number of indirect workers employed?*

ANSWER: Increase in mechanization and/or automation with the increasing demand for technicians and servicemen, increase in paperwork, increase in size of industry with resulting increase in controls.

9. *Why do more unavoidable delays occur in maintenance operations than on production work?*

ANSWER: Because maintenance operations have not been subjected to the same detailed operations analysis studies that have been conducted on production work. Also maintenance work is much less standardized and consequently is subject to more unavoidable delays.

10. *What is meant by crew balance? By interference time?*

ANSWER: Crew balance is the delay time encountered by one member of a crew while waiting for other members of the crew to perform elements of the job. Interference time is the time that a maintenance or other worker is delayed in waiting for others to do necessary work.

11. *Explain how time standards would be established on janitorial operations.*

ANSWER: Use stop-watch study and fundamental motion data to develop standard data for janitorial work such as: sweep, wax and buff floor, wet mop, vacuum rugs, clean, dust and mop lounge, etc.

12. *What office operations are readily time studied?*

ANSWER: File clerks, typing pools, punch card operators, billing groups, tabulating machine operators.

13. *Why are standard data especially applicable to indirect labor operations?*

ANSWER: Indirect labor operations are usually longer than direct labor operations and are non-repetitive. Consequently stop-watch time study is not particularly efficient. The more efficient way to establish standards on indirect labor work is through standard data.

14. *Summarize the advantages of standards established on indirect work.*

ANSWER: Operating improvements can be made, resulting in better operator performance, indirect labor costs can be related to the work load, budgeting of work can be achieved, efficiency of labor groups can be determined, costs can be determined, system and method improvements can be evaluated, incentive wage payment can be installed, indirect labor work can be planned and scheduled, and less supervision will be required.

15. *When were Universal Maintenance Standards first developed? Who first developed them?*

ANSWER: Universal Maintenance Standards were first developed by H. B. Maynard and G. J. Stegmerten in 1955.

16. *Why is work sampling the best technique for establishing supervisory standards?*

ANSWER: It is the least expensive way to establish standards on this type of work that is based on measurement.

17. *Explain the application of "slotting" under a universal standards system.*

ANSWER: In establishing a standard on a work order, the analyst will fit the job to a category or "slot" where similar jobs have been studied and standards established.

18. *Why will a universal standards system involving as few as 20 benchmark standards work in a large maintenance department where thousands of different jobs are performed every year?*

ANSWER: Although thousands of different jobs are performed every year, each of these jobs or a portion of each of these jobs will carry a standard that is quite close in time value to one of the 20 benchmark jobs. If accurate slotting takes place, then reasonably accurate time values for the thousands of different jobs will prevail.

PROBLEMS

1. *Through work measurement procedures, an average time of 6.24 minutes per piece is established on the inspection of a complex forging. The standard deviation of the inspection time is 0.71 minutes. Usually 60 forgings are delivered to the inspection station on the line every eight-hour turn. One operator is used to perform this inspection.*

   Assuming that the castings arrive in Poisson fashion and that the service time is exponential, what would be the mean waiting time of a casting at the inspection station? What would be the average length of the casting queue?

   ANSWER: $s = 1$; $a = \dfrac{60}{480} = 0.125$; $h = 6.24$; $\sigma = 0.71$

   $$u = \frac{(0.125)(6.24)}{1} = 0.78 \text{ servers' occupancy ratio}$$

   $$w = \left[\frac{uh}{2(1 - u)}\right] \left[1 + \left(\frac{\sigma}{h}\right)^2\right]$$

   $$= \left[\frac{(.78)(6.24)}{2(1 - .78)}\right] \left[1 + \left(\frac{0.71}{6.24}\right)^2\right]$$

   $$= (11.062)(1.013)$$

   $$= 11.205 \text{ minutes of average waiting time}$$

   $$L = \frac{1}{1 - u}$$

   $$= 4.545 \text{ average length of queue formed.}$$

2. *In the tool and die room of the Dorben Company, the work measurement analyst wishes to determine a standard for the jig boring of holes on a variety of molds. The standard will be used to estimate mold costs only, and it will be based upon operator wait time for molds coming from a surface grinding section and upon operator machining time. The wait time is based upon: a single server, Poisson arrivals, exponential service time, and first-come, first-served discipline.*

   A study revealed the average time between arrivals to be 58 minutes. The average jig-boring time was found to be 46 minutes. What is the possibility of a delay of a mold at the jig borer? What is the average number of molds in back of the jig borer?

   ANSWER: $a = \dfrac{1}{58} = 0.017$ average number of arrivals/min.

   $h = 46$ minutes mean service time

   $s = 1$ server

   $u = \dfrac{ah}{s} = 0.782$ probability of delay of a mold at the jig borer.

   $L = \dfrac{1}{(1 - u)} = \dfrac{1}{(1 - .782)} = 4.587$ average number of molds in back of jig borer.

23

Work measurement and computers

TEXT QUESTIONS

1. *Explain in detail how an automated methods and standards data processing system can minimize standards' clerical and computational work.*

   ANSWER: Considerable clerical and computational work is saved through the utilization of data processing equipment where the description of each element is retrieved, the normal elemental times are identified, the elemental times are extended by frequencies, allowances are applied, and the allowed time for the operation is computed. All associated reports are prepared by the system.

2. *Outline how a change that affects several operations is introduced when an automated data system is employed.*

   ANSWER: If a standard data element is changed, this change is reflected in the standard data element file. Then the new element description and its new standard time are retrieved for each operation where this standard data element is used. With details of operations stored in a file of magnetic tapes or disks, retrieval techniques allow changes to be made through "add" and/or "delete" instructions.

3. *What two major input files are needed in the installation of a work measurement system?*

   ANSWER: The element file and the operation file.

4. *What helpful management reports can be readily generated if an automated work measurement system is being used?*

   ANSWER: Reports that show the old and new standards for the operations, the variance, and the percentage of variance. Reports that show where specific components, durable and perishable tools are used. Reports providing estimates of time and/or cost. Reports that generate a work-place layout.

GENERAL QUESTIONS

1. *What disadvantages, if any, can exist if an automated work measurement system is installed?*

   SUGGESTED DISCUSSION: Bring out that the initial cost may be too high. This would be true for smaller companies. There is the disadvantage of the time it takes to train capable personnel to operate the system.

2. *What percentage of time do you feel the work measurement analyst would save using the computer technique illustrated in Figure 24–8? Will the keypunch operator make as many input errors as the time study person's arithmetic errors? Why or Why not?*

SUGGESTED DISCUSSION: Probably save 25 to 50 percent of his or her time depending upon the work being studied. The keypunch operator will probably, on the average, make fewer input errors when compared to the time study person's arithmetic errors because arithmetic work by nature is more arduous and subject to error.

PROBLEMS

A NOTE TO THE INSTRUCTOR: The following two elementary problems are programmed in Pascal. It is the feeling that Pascal comes closer to the primary aim of a programming language: "to allow the programmer to formulate thoughts in terms of abstractions suitable to the problem rather than in terms of facilities offered by the hardware."[1] Pascal from the standpoint of nomenclature, flow, and data structures is suited to the work of the methods and work measurement analyst.

1. *Write a computer program to provide output data for the painting of a line of castings from the equation:*

$$T = [c_1 + 0.1625 + n(V_1 + 0.0820)] [1 + 0<]$$

$c_1 = 0.16$ *or* 0.25 *or* 0.38 *depending upon the grade of paint used*

$S = $ *Surface area of casting in square inches*

$n = $ *Number of holes that need to be plugged prior to painting*

$V_1 = 0.04$ *or* 0.07 *or* 0.13 *depending upon the plug diameter*

$O<_1 = 0.12$ *or* 0.15 *or* 0.18, *depending upon which paint booth is used*

[1] *N. Wirth, "Programming Languages: What to Demand and How to Assess Them" BERICHTE DES INSTITUTS FUR INFORMATIK, Vol. 17, March 2, 1976.*

ANSWER:

```
READ (C1, S, N, PLUG, DIAM, BOOTH);
ALPHA: = .18
IF ALPHA = 2 THEN ALPHA: = .15;
IF ALPHA = 1 THEN ALPHA: = .12;
V1 = .13
IF PLUG DIA < 1.5 THEN V1: = .07;
IF PLUG DIA < .75 THEN V: = .04;
T = [C1 + .162 * 3 + N * (V1 + .082)] * (1 + ALPHA)
WRITE (T);
```

Above program based upon $U_1 = .04$ when plug diameter is less than $3/4$ inch; $.07$ when plug diameter is $> 3/4 < 1^1/2$ and $.13$ when plug diameter is $> 1^1/2$.

2. *Prepare a flow diagram and write a computer program to estimate standard times for producing a variety of jigs and fixtures from the equation:*

$$T = 2.5 + 0.14W^2 + 0.75N + 1.82Q + 0.51S + 2.42B + 6.14 + t$$

where:

T = *A time in hours to produce one jig or fixture*
W = *Gross weight of jig or fixture in pounds*
N = *Number of holes jig bored in the tool*
Q = *Number of clamps on the tool*
S = *Number of stops on the tool*
B = *Number of bushings on the tool*
t = *0.25 when tolerances are closer than ± 0.001 inch*
   = *0.10 when tolerances are between ± 0.001 and ± 0.005*
   = *0 when tolerances are greater than ± 0.005*

ANSWER:

```
READ (W, N, Q, S, B, TOLER);
TT: = 0.;
IF TOLER < .005 THEN TT: = .1;
IF TOLER < .001 THEN TT: = .25;
T: = SQRT (2.5 + .14 * W * * 2) + .75 * N + 1.82 * Q + .51 * S + 2.42 *
B + 6.14 + TT;
WRITE (T);
```

24

Follow-up method and uses of time standards

TEXT QUESTIONS

1. *Explain the use of learning curves in the "follow-up" step of the systematic approach to motion and time study.*

   ANSWER: Learning curves can predict operator performance improvement due to learning. In the follow-up, the analyst should determine if the anticipated improvement in operator output is being realized.

2. *In what different ways may time standards be determined?*

   ANSWER: By estimate, by performance records, by stop-watch time study, by standard data, by time formulas, by work sampling, and by queuing theory.

3. *How can valid time standards help develop an ideal plant layout?*

   ANSWER: By knowing the exact requirements for facilities in terms of numbers, style, and load, the best possible utilization of space can be determined.

4. *Explain the relationship between time standards and plant capacity.*

   ANSWER: With time standards, it is a matter of simple arithmetic to determine the capacity of a machine, a department, and the entire plant. Department and plant capacity can be easily determined by calculating the capacity of bottle-neck operations only.

5. *In what way are time standards used for effective production control?*

   ANSWER: Production control involves scheduling, routing, and expediting. Time standards are the basis of all scheduling including long-range, firm-order, and detailed-operation scheduling.

6. *How do time standards allow the accurate determination of labor costs?*

   ANSWER: Labor costs are accurately determined by multiplying the reciprocal of the efficiency of the section or department by the average daywork hourly rate. This would give the hourly direct labor cost based on standard production. Under incentive wage payment the standard multiplied by the base rate would provide the direct labor cost based upon standard production.

123

7. *How does developing time standards help maintain the quality of product?*

ANSWER: Since production standards are based upon the quantity of acceptable pieces produced in a unit of time, and since no credit is given for defective work turned out, workers make an effort to produce only quality parts.

8. *In what way is customer service bettered through valid time standards?*

ANSWER: Time standards will make a product more competitive and consequently allow it to be sold at a lower price. With time standards, better production control is effected resulting in meeting customer delivery requirements. Usually quality will be assured in a sound standards program.

9. *What is the relation between labor cost and efficiency?*

ANSWER: The greater the efficiency, the less the unit direct labor cost under daywork wage payment. Under one-for-one incentive wage payment, the unit direct labor cost remains constant beyond standard.

10. *If a daywork shop was paying an average rate of $12.75 per hour and had 250 direct labor employees working, what would be the true direct labor cost per hour if during a normal month 40,000 hours of work were produced?*

ANSWER: 250 employees × 173 hours per month = 43,250 clock hours

$$40,000/43,250 = 0.92 \text{ efficiency.}$$

$$\$12.74/0.92 = \$13.86 \text{ actual cost/hr. based upon standard production}$$

11. *How are management problems simplified through the application of time standards?*

ANSWER: Having reliable time standards management can introduce many control measures that otherwise would be difficult to exercise—for example, scheduling, material control, budgeting, forecasting, standard costs.

12. *In what way did President Truman provide emphasis for the use of time standards in governmental operations?*

ANSWER: See Chapter 2. It was under the Truman administration that a bill was passed which allowed the War Department to use time study, and in 1949 the prohibition against using stop-watches was dropped from appropriation language.

13. *Explain how inventory and storage areas can be predicted accurately?*

ANSWER: Time standards allow the accurate computation of machine, department, and plant capacity. This information supplemented with demand requirements allows the calculation of in-process storage and inventory based upon economic lot size and economic order quantity.

GENERAL QUESTIONS

1. *What other uses of time standards not mentioned in this chapter can be realized?*

REMARKS: Place a list on the board. Such functions as product engineering and preventive maintenance may be improved with sound standards.

2. *What is the relationship between the accuracy of time standards and production control? Does the law of diminishing returns apply?*

ANSWER: The students should recognize that for good production control, accurate standards should prevail. However production control would be improved very little, if any, by having standards refined to the 0.001 minute. The law of diminishing returns certainly applies.

3. *How does work measurement improve the selection and placement of personnel?*

ANSWER: Bring out that with measured time standards, operators are expected to perform at least to standard. New employees are often selected and assigned work based upon dexterity testing, which helps assure that operators will be able to achieve standard in work assignments that are to their capability and liking.

4. *When is it no longer necessary to follow up the installed method?*

ANSWER: The students should recognize that followup is a continuing procedure and will take place at intervals during the life of the method.

5. *Do you believe that the typical worker today is motivated if the company goals and objectives are clearly presented to him? Discuss and give examples.*

ANSWER: The instructor should develop this question and monitor the discussion. In view of the current international competition, the typical worker today is motivated by learning of his company's goals and objectives.

PROBLEMS

1. *In the XYZ Manufacturing Company, direct labor cost is based on the efficiency relationship illustrated in Figure 24–6. For a given product line, the selling price was based upon the company's running at 95 percent efficiency. How much additional profit did the company realize if the actual efficiency turned out to be 110 percent? Profit was originally estimated at 10 percent of the total cost. On this product line, the total overhead was estimated to be 100 percent of prime cost (direct labor plus direct material). Material cost averaged $5 per unit of output, and direct labor averaged 0.50 hours per unit of output.*

ANSWER: From Figure 24–6: 95% = $6.56 labor cost/hr.
$$110\% = \$5.76 \text{ labor cost/hr.}$$

Prime cost/unit = $5.00 + (0.50)(6.56) = $ 8.28
Overhead   =   8.28
                                           $16.56

         Profit $ 1.66/unit

At 110% Prime cost/unit = $5.00 + (0.50)(5.76) = $ 7.88
Overhead   7.88
                                           $15.76

$16.56 − $15.76 = $0.80 additional profit
$ 1.66 + $0.80 = $2.46 profit/unit at 110% efficiency.

2. *What would be the costing rate in the finishing department of the XYZ Company where 32 employees work? Twenty-seven of these employees are on standard and have been averaging 1,310 hours earned per standard 40-hour week. The daywork hourly rate for these workers is $13.00 per hour. The remaining 5 workers are line supervisors who are not on standard. Their daywork hourly rate is $15.20 per hour.*

ANSWER:

$$\frac{1}{1,310 \div [(27)(40)]} \times \$13.00 = \$10.72 \text{ standard rate of employees on standard}$$

$$\frac{(5)(\$15.20)}{27} = \$2.82 \text{ supervisor rate in department per standard employee}$$

$10.72 + $2.82 = $13.54/hour costing rate

3. *In the XYZ Company, management is considering going from two 8-hour shifts per day to three 8-hour shifts per day or two 10-hour shifts per day in order to increase capacity. Management realizes that shift start-up results in a loss of productivity that averages 0.5 hour per employee. The premium for the third shift is 15 percent per hour. Time over eight hours worked per day gives the operator 50 percent more pay. In order to meet projected demands, it is necessary to increase the work-hours of production by 25 percent. In view of insufficient space and capital equipment, this increase cannot be accommodated by increasing the number of employees on either the first or the second shift. How should management proceed?*

    ANSWER: Let X = current production per 8 hour shift.

          Required production then equals $(1.25)(2X) = 2.5X$

          Therefore third shift would need to accommodate $0.5X$

          Two 10 hour shifts would take care of this extra $0.5X$ required production at an *extra* labor cost of (0.5)(Rate of operator) (2 hours)(Number of employees on two shifts).

This cost must be compared to the *extra* cost of the third shift.

$$\frac{(0.15)(\text{Rate of operator})(8 \text{ Hours})(\text{Number of employees on one shift})}{2}$$

Is: $(0.5)(R)(2)(N)$ less than $(0.15)(R)(4)(N)$

$RN > 0.6RN$

$\therefore$ Third shift with $\dfrac{X}{2}$ employees would be more economical.

25

Wage payment

TEXT QUESTIONS

1. *Under what three general classes may the majority of wage incentive plans be classified?*

   ANSWER: Direct financial plans, indirect financial plans, plans other than financial.

2. *Differentiate between individual wage payment plans and group-type plans.*

   ANSWER: In individual plans, each employee's compensation is governed by his/her own performance. Group plans are applicable to two or more persons who are working as a team on operations that tend to be dependent on one another.

3. *What is meant by the term fringe benefits?*

   ANSWER: The portion of tangible compensation given by the employer to employees that is not paid in the form of wages, salaries, or bonuses. These include insurance, retirement funds, and other employee services.

4. *What company policies are included under nonfinancial incentives?*

   ANSWER: Periodic shop conferences, quality control circles, proper employee placement, job enrichment, job enlargement, nonfinancial suggestion plans, ideal working conditions.

5. *What are the characteristics of piecework? Plot the unit cost curve and operator earning curve for daywork and piecework on the same set of coordinates.*

   ANSWER: Standards are expressed in terms of money, operators are rewarded in direct proportion to output, and the base rate is not guaranteed.

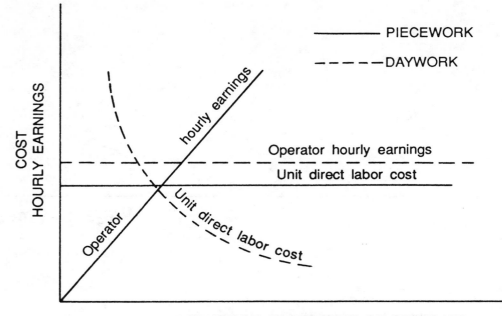

PRODUCTION IN PERCENT OF STANDARD

6. *Why did measured daywork become popular in the 1930s?*

   ANSWER: To get away from piecework that was initiated in the era of the "efficiency expert."

7. *Define profit sharing.*

   ANSWER: A procedure where an employer pays to all employees, in addition to good rates of regular pay, special current or deferred sums based not only upon individual or group performance, but on the prosperity of the business as a whole.

8. *What specific type of profit sharing plan has received general acceptance?*

   ANSWER: No one specific type of profit sharing has received general industrial acceptance.

9. *What three broad categories cover the majority of profit sharing installations?*

   ANSWER: Cash plans, deferred plans, combined plans.

10. *Under the cash plan, upon what does the amount of money distributed depend?*

    ANSWER: Upon the degree of financial success of the enterprise for the bonus period.

11. *What determines the length of the period between bonus payments under the cash plan? Why is it poor practice to have the period too long? What disadvantages are there to the short period?*

    ANSWER: A period long enough to reflect the status of the business, the amount of cash that will be shared. If the period is too long, there will be insufficient connection between effort and financial reward. The short period may provide too small a reward so that employees will lose interest in the plan.

12. *What are the characteristic features of the deferred profit sharing plan?*

    ANSWER: Periodic investments of the profits of the business for the employees, so that upon retirement or separation from the company, they will have a source of income at a time when their needs may be more pronounced.

128

13. *Why is the "share and share alike" method of distribution not particularly common? On what basis is this technique advocated by its proponents?*

ANSWER: Because employees within an organization do not contribute uniformly and consequently should not share alike in the company's success.

Proponents of this method believe that individual base rates have already taken care of the relative importance of the different workers. This method will supply a feeling of teamwork.

14. *What 10 principles summarized by the Council for Profit Sharing Industries are fundamental for a successful profit sharing plan?*

REMARKS: See text.

15. *Why have many unions shown an antagonistic attitude toward profit sharing?*

ANSWER: When practiced with harmony between labor and management, in the eyes of labor it minimizes the need for a union. Some unions feel that profit sharing is a wage cutting method.

16. *What suggestions has James Lincoln offered for those embarking on an incentive installation?*

REMARKS: See seven points in text.

17. *What advantages does the Rucker plan have over the Scanlon plan?*

ANSWER: The Rucker plan encourages employees to conserve supplies and materials since they would benefit from these savings. Also the Rucker plan, unlike the Scanlon plan, partially accounts for variables such as product mix.

18. *How does Improshare differ from the Rucker and the Scanlon plans?*

ANSWER: To begin with, Improshare does not emphasize employee involvement as do the Rucker and Scanlon plans. Also, Improshare is based on the number of work hours saved for a given number of units produced. These work hours saved are based upon comparing the number of hours required to produce the same number of units to the actual hours worked. The Rucker plan is based upon savings in the production value added, while the Scanlon plan considers the ratio of payroll costs to the value of production.

19. *How does job enrichment differ from job enlargement?*

ANSWER: Job enrichment implies increasing the depth of responsibility and skill required to perform a job, while job enlargement increases the breadth of responsibility and skill.

20. *Why is it usually advisable to have a range of pay rates that are applicable to each job?*

ANSWER: To provide for seniority or service, reliability, attendance, and quality of production.

21. *What four important hypotheses related to motivation should the work measurement analyst be cognizant of?*

ANSWER: People basically want to work and to achieve, they want to be involved in the achievement of the goals established by their organization, they will perform better if given both independence and control in their work situation, and they expect to see a relationship between their rewards and contributions.

22. *Why do many union officials prefer straight daywork as a form of wage payment?*

ANSWER: They would prefer to bargain for base rate (daywork) increases than get involved with all the problems that can arise through incentive installation.

23. *What are the fundamental prerequisites of a successful wage incentive plan?*

ANSWER: Policy providing for valid work measurement must first be introduced, adequate volume of work must be available for each operator (this implies good scheduling and inventory control), base rates must be fair, adequate tools and well maintained equipment must be available.

24. *What are the requisites of a sound wage incentive system?*

ANSWER: Provide opportunity to earn approximately 20 to 35 percent above the base rate, be simple to understand and apply, guarantee the base rate, which should be established by job evaluation, have a range of base rates associated with each job class, have paychecks that show both the regular and incentive earnings, make provisions for unavoidable loss in time not included in the standard.

25. *What is extra allowance or "blue ticket" time? How may it be controlled?*

ANSWER: This is nonproductive time due to machine breakdowns, material shortages, tool difficulties, etc. that are not covered in the allowances applied to the individual time standards.

26. *Why is it fundamental to keep time standards up-to-date if a wage incentive plan is to succeed?*

ANSWER: Obsolete standards will result in wage payments that are not equitable. Loose time rates will provide take-home pay that is excessive, which will lead to the failure of the system and perhaps the business.

27. *What does unduly high performance indicate?*

ANSWER: A creeping looseness in standards and/or the introduction of a methods change for which no standard revision has been made.

28. *What responsibilities of the foreman, time study department, quality control department, production department, accounting department, and industrial relations department are essential to the effective administration of a sound wage incentive system?*

ANSWER: The foreman needs to ascertain that correct methods are being used, that accurate piece counts prevail, and that the workers understand all details of the system. The time study department has the responsibility of developing good standards, high incentive coverage of direct and indirect work, and simplified compensation formula. The quality control department has the responsibility of maintaining good in-process inspection and overall quality control. The production department has the responsibility of maintaining good production control including inventory control and good scheduling so as to assure ample work for the entire force under an incentive environment. The accounting department should provide information on excessive earnings of departments and operators as well as overall efficiency. The industrial relations department needs to assure that only qualified and trained operators are assigned incentive opportunities, that equitable base rates prevail, that cooperation with the union exists, and that everyone is advised as to how the incentive system operates.

29. *What 16 fundamental principles should be followed in order to assure a successful wage payment plan?*

REMARKS: See text.

30. *When would it be inadvisable to put an indirect labor activity on incentive?*

ANSWER: If the work cannot be readily measured, if the volume of available work is insufficient to economically justify an incentive installation, and if the cost of measuring the output is excessive.

31. *How would you go about establishing a climate for worker motivation?*

ANSWER: Provide a management style that emphasizes a supporting role rather than a directive role. Clearly establish the goals of the enterprise. Initiate a policy to provide regular feedback to all employees. Assure that work stations are designed so that the operator is in a position to control to a large extent the assignment he has been given.

GENERAL QUESTIONS

1. *Why do many unions object to management posting incentive earnings?*

   ANSWER: Discuss this question in detail. Some unions feel this procedure will "pit worker against worker" and result in higher performance for the same rate of pay.

2. *Should indirect labor that is not on incentive carry a higher base rate than direct labor on incentive when both jobs carry the same evaluation? Why or Why not?*

   ANSWER: This is another question worthy of much discussion. Many companies will pay a higher base rate for the same job for those not on incentive, the reason being to reduce the spread on take home pay. The question then becomes, why should we pay more per hour for standard performance than the job is worth?

3. *What is the major reason that causes many union officials to disfavor any form of incentive wage payment?*

   ANSWER: A well run incentive system will result in high earnings for the employees. The typical union feels that high wages are the most important reason for their existence. Thus if high wages are received with incentives, the rank and file employee will question the necessity of a union and the resulting union dues.

4. *How can the piece count be controlled within the plant?*

   ANSWER: Take time to discuss this with the class in detail. Review "weigh counting," foreman spot-checking the operator count, the use of standard size containers that take a fixed number of parts to fill them, attaching mechanical or electrical counters to the facility, etc.

5. *How can a yardstick of performance be established in the following jobs: tool crib attendant, tool grinder, floor sweeper, chip-hauler?*

   ANSWER: Bring out that on most indirect jobs there may be more than one yardstick of performance. Some yardsticks that may be used on the above jobs include:

   Tool crib attendant: number of operators serviced and their mean performance; number of tools dispensed.
   Tool grinder: number and type of tools ground; number of operators serviced and their mean performance.
   Floor sweeper: square feet of floor space serviced; number of operators being serviced with clean floor space.
   Chip-hauler: pounds of chips removed; number of machine operators serviced.

6. *Explain how you would enrich the position of "punch press operator."*

   ANSWER: Bring out that enrichment implies "depth" while enlargement implies "breadth." The punch press operator could be enriched by having him set up his own punch press, by sample inspecting the parts coming off the press.

PROBLEMS

1. *In a single product plant where Improshare was installed, 411 employees produced 14,672 product units over a one-year period. 802,000 clock hours were recorded over this period. In a given week, 425 employees worked a total of 16,150 hours and produced 348 units. What would be the hourly value of this output? What would be the unit labor cost in hours for this week's production?*

   ANSWER: 802,000 clock hours/14,672 product units = 54.66 hrs./unit

   16,150 hrs./54.66 hrs./unit = 295.46 units, the standard output

   348 units × 54.66 = 19,021.68 hrs. value of output

   Gain = 19,021.68 − 16,150 = 2,871.68 hrs.

   0.5 × 2,871.68 = 1,435.84 hrs., the workers' share of gain

   1,435.84/16,150 = 0.089 = 8.9%, percentage bonus

   $$\frac{16,150 + 1,435.84}{348} = 50.53 \text{ hrs./unit labor cost}$$

2. *An allowed time of 0.0125 hours/piece is established for machining a small component. A setup time of 0.32 hours is established also, as the operator performs the necessary setup work on "incentive." Compute:*

   a. Total time allowed to complete an order of 860 pieces.

   b. Operator efficiency, if job is completed in an eight-hour day.

   c. Efficiency of the operator if he requires 12 hours to complete the job.

   ANSWER: (a) 0.32 + (0.0125)(860) = 11.07 hours

   (b) 11.07 ÷ 8 = 138%

   (c) 11.07 ÷ 12 = 92%

3. *A "one-for-one" or 100 percent time premium plan for incentive payment is in operation. The operator base rate for this class of work is $10.40. The base rate is guaranteed. Compute:*

   (a) Total earnings for the job at the efficiency determined in problem 2(b).

   (a) Hourly earnings, from above.

   (b) Total earnings for job at the efficiency determined in problem 2(c).

   (c) Direct labor cost per piece from (a), excluding setup.

   (d) Direct labor cost per piece from (c), excluding setup.

   ANSWER: (a) 11.07 × 10.40 = $115.128

   (b) 115.128/8 = $14.391

   (c) 12 × 10.40 = $124.80

   (d) 0.0125 × 10.40 = $0.13

   (e) (10.40 × 0.0125) ÷ 0.92 = $0.1413

4. *A forging operation is studied, and a rate of 0.42 minute per piece is set. The operator works on the job for a full eight-hour day and produces 1,500 pieces.*

   (a) How many standard hours does the operator earn?

   (b) What is his efficiency for the day?

   (c) If his base rate is $9.80 per hour, compute his earnings for the day. (Use a 100 percent time premium plan.)

   (d) What is the direct labor cost per piece at this efficiency?

   (e) What would be the proper piece rate (rate expressed in money) for this job, assuming that the above time standard is correct?

   ANSWER: (a) $(0.42 \times 1,500) \div 60 = 10.5$ hours

   (b) $10.5/8 = 131\%$

   (c) $\$9.8 \times 10.5 = \$102.90$ earnings for the day

   (d) $102.90/1,500 = \$0.0686$ direct labor cost per piece

   (e) $0.0686

5. *A 60–40 gain sharing plan is in operation in a plant. The established time value on a certain job is 0.75 minute, and the base rate is $8.80. What is the direct labor cost per piece when the operator efficiency is:*

   (a) 50 percent of standard

   (b) 80 percent of standard

   (c) 100 percent of standard

   (d) 120 percent of standard

   (e) 160 percent of standard

   ANSWER: (a) $100/50 \times 0.75/60 \times 8.80 = \$0.22$

   (b) $100/80 \times 0.75/60 \times 8.80 = \$0.1375$

   (c) $100/100 \times 0.75/60 \times 8.80 = \$0.11$

   (d) $100/120 \times 0.75/60 \times 8.80 + 0.6 \times 8.80 \times (0.75/60 - 0.625/60) = \$.1027$

   (e) $100/160 \times 0.75/60 \times 8.80 + 0.6 \times 8.80 \times (0.75/60 - 0.469/60) = \$.0936$

6. *A worker is employed in a plant where all the rates are set on a money basis (piece rates). He is regularly employed at a job where the guaranteed base rate is $8.80. His regular earnings are in excess of $88.00 per day. Due to the pressure of work, he is asked to help out on another job, classified so that it pays $10.00 per hour. He works three days on this job and earns $80.00 each day.*

   (a) How much should the operator be paid for each day's work on this new job? Why?

   (b) Would it make any difference if he had worked on a new job where the base rate was $8.00 per hour and had earned $72.00? Explain.

   ANSWER: If the operator will be able to stay on the better job, he should be paid $80.00 per day—what he earned. However, if he was assigned this new job for just three days, then he should be paid his average hourly earnings while on his regular job, that is $88.00 per day.

   If assigned a lower paid job for a short period, such as $8.00 per hour, he should be paid his regular average earnings of $88.00 per day.

7. An incentive plan employing a "low-rate high-rate" differential is in use. A certain class of work has the guaranteed "low-rate" of $6.00 per hour and the "high-rate" for work on standard of $9.20 per hour. A job is studied and a rate of 0.036 hours per piece is set. What is the direct labor cost per piece at the following efficiencies?:

(a) 50 percent

(b) 80 percent

(c) 98 percent

(d) 105 percent

(e) 150 percent

ANSWER: (a) $100/50 \times 0.036 \times 6 = \$0.432$

(b) $100/80 \times 0.036 \times 6 = \$0.27$

(c) $100/98 \times 0.036 \times 6 = \$0.2204$

(d) $100/105 \times 0.036 \times 9.2 = \$0.3154$

(e) $100/150 \times 0.036 \times 9.2 = \$0.2208$

26

Training and research for methods, time study, and wage payment

TEXT QUESTIONS

1. *Outline the objectives of the typical labor union.*

   ANSWER: To secure for its members higher wage levels, decreased working hours per work week, increased social and fringe benefits, improved working conditions, and job security.

2. *Why have unions in the past sought flat "across-the-board" wage increases for their members?*

   ANSWER: Because it was not to their advantage to emphasize differences in workers' abilities and interests; to do this would increase rivalries and jealousies among their members and potential members.

3. *Explain why the union training program says that time study is an "imprecise tool and lends itself to easy abuse."*

   ANSWER: This statement encourages typical workers to feel a need for union membership to protect them from managerial abuses that can affect their earnings.

4. *What are the four approaches to time study suggested by the typical union?*

   ANSWER: Prevent time study altogether, allow management to use any method of setting job standards but reserve the right to bargain on the results, participate with management in setting standards, allow management to make time studies but insist on bargaining on both the methods used and their applications.

5. *What three points related to the psychological and sociological reactions of the operator should be recognized by the analyst?*

   ANSWER: Most people do not respond favorably to change, job security is uppermost in most workers' minds, people have a need for affiliation and consequently are influenced by the group to which they belong.

6. *What do we mean by "the human approach"?*

   ANSWER: The approach that recognizes three fundamental needs of all people: achievement, affiliation, and power.

7. *In what 12 ways can you get people to agree with your ideas?*

   REMARKS: See text.

8. *Is methods training conducted within a plant self-supporting?*

ANSWER: Experience has proven that sound methods training within a plant is almost always self-supporting.

9. *Why is plantwide training in the areas of methods and time study a healthy management step?*

ANSWER: Because when the theories, techniques, and economic necessity of methods, work measurement, and employee motivation are understood by all parties, little difficulty will be encountered in their application.

10. *Why should training in time study be looked upon as a continuing project?*

ANSWER: To take advantage of new developments, which are constantly being made, to acquaint new operating and supervisory members of the plant with the philosophies and techniques of time and motion study, and to maintain accuracy in performance rating of the various time study personnel.

11. *Why is American industry more receptive to the time study analyst today than it was prior to World War II?*

ANSWER: Because of its proven utility, because of favorable support from the federal government, and because of the growth in stature of the industrial engineer.

12. *What order of importance does diversified industry place upon time study in the development of an industrial engineering curriculum?*

ANSWER: They still feel training in this area is of top importance.

13. *What intangible benefits can be achieved through a methods training program on the foreman level?*

ANSWER: Foremen will be more receptive to the work of the methods analyst, will be less resistant to change, and will take a more supportive roll in connection with management innovations.

14. *Why should the experienced analyst be continually checked on his ability to performance rate?*

ANSWER: To make certain that his conception of normal is not deviating from standard.

15. *How can a person develop creative ability?*

ANSWER: Train yourself to be observant. Get in the habit of asking how things are made, why parts are designed as they are, what materials are used and why.

16. *What are some of the areas where research needs to be done in methods? In standards? In job evaluation?*

REMARKS: See text.

17. *What is meant by "local and grand stability"?*

ANSWER: See text. Ambruzzi recommends that the method and performance be stabilized before taking a time study. The importance of Ambruzzi's recommendation can be appreciated if one is familiar with learning curve theory. Of course, the purpose of performance rating is to take care of the variation in performance due to skill, effort, and conditions.

18. *Explain how the videotape recorder can be used in concert with the computer.*

ANSWER: The digitizing of video information for computer analysis can be used to evaluate alternatives in the design of a work station. Once an ideal work center is developed, the videotape recorder through the digitizing of video information will be able to develop a fair work standard and provide hard copy of details related to the method.

136

GENERAL QUESTIONS

1. *Who should handle in-plant training in methods, time study, and wage payment?*

   ANSWER: The industrial relations department should be responsible for coordinating the training. The actual instruction can be shared with qualified industrial engineers in the I. E. department and outside expertise. Often university professors make excellent choices to handle the instruction.

2. *Is it advisable to provide training in the area of methods, time study and wage payment down to the operator level? Why or Why not?*

   ANSWER: Yes, it is a good idea to provide training down to the operator level. Usually, the training at the operator level will not be nearly as detailed as that given line supervision and other members of the management team.

3. *To what opportunities within an industry can the experienced analyst in methods and time study expect to be promoted?*

   ANSWER: The instructor can give several examples from his own experience. Typical promotions can be to: line supervision, industrial relations, etc.

4. *What is the relationship between work measurement and operations research?*

   ANSWER: There is a close relationship since much of the data used in the solution of operations research problems is supplied by the work measurement analyst. It is not unusual to have a work measurement analyst on an operations research team.

5. *Will "automation" diminish the need for the methods and time study analyst?*

   REMARKS: Spend some time discussing this question. Certainly with complete automation, there is little need for the methods and time study analyst. However, there will always be considerable work that is accomplished without complete automation.

6. *What government legislation has changed the status of labor unions?*

   REMARKS: Discuss this in detail. You might want to bring out the current status of the Professional Air Traffic Controllers Organization; the union's legal right to time study information as established by decisions of arbitrators and the National Labor Relations Board; etc.

7. *Why do unions often train their own time study men?*

   ANSWER: They prefer to emphasize those aspects of the procedure (rating and allowances) that can lead to both inconsistent and inaccurate standards. Having a thorough background in these areas of the time study procedure can be advantageous in connection with rate disputes.

8. *Would a young engineer find the work in the time study division of the CIO a challenging opportunity? Why or Why not?*

   ANSWER: This would depend largely upon the individual. Certainly the young analyst can make a major contribution in the productivity of the country by taking a job with a union and using his education and training to develop a more harmonious relationship between labor and management. Today with world wide competition making it difficult for many companies to stay in business, one of the best ways to provide a competitive edge is through the application of methods based on the best technology, fair standards, and incentives (either financial or other) supported by a competent management team in cooperation with a supportive union.

9. *Will the typical stop-watch (mechanical and/or electronic) be obsolete by the year 2000? Why?*

ANSWER: The typical stop-watch will not be used nearly as much by the year 2000. However, because of its portability and convenience to enter all types of work environments, it will continue to be used.

PROBLEMS

1. *Based upon the cost relationships presented in this chapter, what would be the total annual dollar savings (estimated) of a company having an annual direct labor payroll of $2,500,000 and a fixed burden rate of 150 percent of direct labor if it initiated a methods and standards program?*

ANSWER: See data in text. Assume an improvement of 25 percent in productivity or 20 units of direct labor per hundred employees. Let us estimate direct labor cost with fringe benefits to be $20/hr. or $40,000/yr. Extra cost to introduce a methods and standards program per 100 employees = 8 units. Net savings based on direct labor alone = 20 units − 8 units = 12 units. 12 units × $40,000 = $480,000 savings per year.

Fixed burden per unit of output reduced to 80 percent of former rate. Twenty percent savings of (1.5)(2,500,000) = (0.2)(1.5)(2,500,000) = $750,000 savings.

$480,000 + $750,000 = $1,230,000 savings.

Note this total savings would only be possible if there were a demand for the added productivity.

2. *A company employing straight daywork as a method of wage payment is compensating its employees an average of $18.00 per hour. In addition, the cost of fringe benefits is running 30 percent of direct labor. Overhead in this company is 125 percent of direct labor. A methods, standards, and incentive plan is being contemplated in which the average incentive earnings have been estimated as equaling 20 percent of base wages. What payoff will the proposed plan yield?*

ANSWER: Calculate savings per 100 employees prior to initiation of the incentive plan.

Gross direct labor savings per 100 employees =	20 units
Added cost to carry on the program per 100 employees =	8 units
Net savings of direct labor =	12 units
20 percent savings of overhead = (0.2)(1.25)(100) =	25 units
Total savings =	37 units

37 × 2000 hrs./yr. × 1.3 × $18 = $1,731,600/yr./100 employees

With incentive earnings of 20 percent, there will be 20 percent more productivity beyond the 125 units achieved with the introduction of methods and standards or 150 units over which to spread the burden. So now the burden becomes $100/150$ or $2/3$ of the former rate.

This is a $1/3$ saving or (0.333)(1.25)(100) = 41.66 units

Total savings with incentive = 41.66 + 12 = 53.66 units

53.66 × 2000 hrs./yr. × 1.3 × $18 = $2,511,288 savings/100 employees/yr.